ERRORS, MEASUREMENT AND RESULTS IN CHEMICAL ANALYSIS

THE VAN NOSTRAND
SERIES IN ANALYTICAL CHEMISTRY

Edited by

DR. R. A. CHALMERS
Department of Chemistry, University of Aberdeen

This series is designed as a coverage of reliable analytical information of value
to chemists in research, industry and teaching. Each volume is carefully
selected and planned as a modern treatment of a topic of importance to analytical
chemists today. New volumes will be added from time to time.

ERRORS, MEASUREMENT AND RESULTS IN CHEMICAL ANALYSIS

K. ECKSCHLAGER, M. Sc., D. Ph.

Translation Editor: Dr. R. A. CHALMERS
University of Aberdeen

VAN NOSTRAND REINHOLD COMPANY
LONDON
NEW YORK   TORONTO   MELBOURNE

543
E 19

VAN NOSTRAND REINHOLD COMPANY LTD.
Windsor House, 46 Victoria Street, London S.W. 1

INTERNATIONAL OFFICES
New York   Toronto   Melbourne

CONTENTS

6

ACKNOWLEDGEMENT

The author is grateful for permission to reprint the following material.
Tables 4.4 and 4.9 reprinted from *Analytical Chemistry,* 1951, **23,** 636. Copyright 1951 by the American Chemical Society. Reprinted by permission of the copyright owner. Table 4.6 reprinted from CRUMPLER and YOE, *Chemical Computation and Errors,* Wiley, New York, 1946. Reprinted by permission of the copyright owner.
Table 4.12 reprinted from *Biometrika,* 1947, **34.** 41. Reprinted by permission of the copyright holder.
Table 4.20 reprinted from WILCOXON, *Some Rapid Approximate Statistical Procedures,* Ann. Reviews Inc., Stanford, 1949. Reprinted by permission of the copyright holder.

Chapter 1

GENERAL SURVEY OF THE ERRORS OF CHEMICAL ANALYSES

1.1 The significance of determining the errors of results of chemical analyses

The present situation in the chemical industry necessitates rapid and at the same time reliable analytical control of the entire course of production processes, from raw materials through intermediate products up to the final product. The great practical significance of such control is indicated by the evolution of analytical chemistry itself, which we are witnessing at present: new, perfected methods and processes are being worked out, modern instruments and reagents are being applied, more and more perfect apparatus and high-purity reagents are being developed for analytical laboratories, well-established methods are being standardized, so that analytical control has at present — especially in some fields — achieved a high degree of perfection and precision. Of course, it is impossible to eliminate errors in chemical analyses totally: but it is of advantage to be able at least to determine the magnitude and orientation of these errors, in order to have more definite, concrete knowledge of the reliability of our results.

While analytical methods are being perfected, demands on analytical chemists are also rising. It is no longer sufficient today for an analyst to be able to carry out an analysis reliably according to a given procedure: he must also be able himself to select a correct procedure and it is often required of him to be able to assess the results obtained. Frequently, an experienced analyst is able to estimate the extent to which his results agree with the actual content of the component to be determined, but such estimates tend to be rather subjective at times. It is far more reliable and objective to calculate the errors. The possibility of such a calculation is given by the general theory of error, and final assessment of analytical results is allowed by the methods of mathematical statistics. Moreover, these calculations are frequently far less complicated than is generally assumed.

1.2 Errors to which the results of chemical analyses are subject

The fact that errors exist which always accompany analytical results may best be demonstrated by carrying out a number of parallel determinations on one perfectly homogeneous sample, when results will be obtained which, with few exceptions, mutually somewhat differ. This may be explained precisely by the fact that each result is subject to an error which differs somewhat from those of the other results [74]. Errors of chemical analyses are generally classified according to the way in which they affect the result, as (i) *random*, (ii) *systematic*, (iii) *gross errors*.

Random errors, which accompany every determination, are quite irregular and generally small, so that their mean value does not distort the result as compared to the correct value, and they only cause the results of parallel determinations to differ somewhat from each other and from the mean result. We do not know the causes of random errors exactly, but we explain them as consequences of the influence of very small and irregular so-called elementary errors, which originate in the individual operations of an analytical procedure. It is frequently possible to find a suitable mathematical model for the probability distribution of random errors, which allows us to assess their influence on the final result of the analysis by means of the parametric methods of mathematical statistics. If such a model cannot be found, non-parametric statistical methods may sometimes be used.

On the other hand, *systematic errors* are of constant character, they distort the results always in a certain sense, and arise in the method through lack of precision in some instrument or through its incorrect usage, insufficient purity of some reagent (which is a frequent case in trace analysis) etc. Frequently it is possible to establish the cause of a systematic error and remove the error by modifying the procedure, using a different instrument or replacing part of the apparatus, by using reagents of different origin, purifying the reagents or subtracting the value of a blank experiment. We resort to the use of various corrections only in exceptional cases [12].

Gross errors should be distinguished from these two categories of errors, and originate by mistakes in the analytical process or are caused by insufficient care by the analyst. Gross errors may, however, also be caused by unsuitable storage of the sample, incorrect selection of the method, or a numerical error in the calculation of the analytical result. The occurrence of a gross error in only one of several parallel determinations seriously affects the accuracy of the final result.

From a practical point of view it is useful to classify errors as *corrigible* and *incorrigible*, as done by CRUMPLER and YOE [5]: it is important for us to consider the corrigibility of some systematic errors by experimental means.

It is of course impossible to set up an absolute classification of the errors to which results of chemical analyses are subject, because there is a continuous transition between the individual types of errors. The classification into random, systematic and gross errors will, however, later facilitate the application of the methods of mathematical statistics as well as the decision as to which statistical test to use.

1.3 Precision and accuracy of the results of chemical analyses

When assessing the final results, it is necessary to judge (i) their *precision* and (ii) their *accuracy* [18].

We regard results as *precise* if those of a number of parallel determinations agree well mutually, while we regard results as *accurate* if they agree well with the actual content of the component in question (i.e. they are not subject to a systematic error). The terms precision and accuracy of results are illustrated in Fig. 1.1: the individual points denote results of individual determinations, the full-drawn vertical line (μ) denotes the

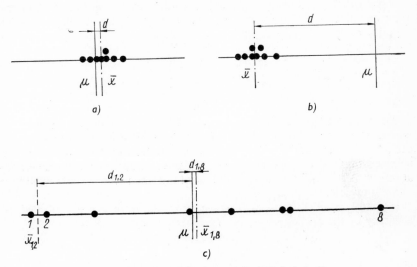

FIG. 1.1. Precision and accuracy of analytical results

(a) The results are precise and accurate, μ is the correct value, $\bar{x}$ is the mean of the results obtained. (b) The results are precise but inaccurate, d is the systematic error. (c) The results are not precise, but their mean value is accurate.

correct value and the interrupted line denotes the value obtained as the mean of the individual results ($\bar{x}$). Of course the most favourable methods are those which give precise and at the same time accurate results (Fig. 1.1a): the results agree well mutually, while the difference between the real and the determined values is small. Inaccurate yet precise results (Fig. 1.1b) agree well mutually, but the final result obtained as their mean value differs somewhat from the actual value (all determinations are subject to a certain systematic error). Non-precise results (Fig. 1.1c) are scattered around the true value. In practice, results that are precise but subject to a small systematic error are often more useful than results with an accurate mean value but low precision. In the first case we know with certainty that the values determined are for example somewhat high, and sometimes we can actually find out how much they differ from the true value, while in the second case we know nothing but that the mean value is of low reliability.

1.4 Absolute and relative errors

The expression *absolute (simple) error, d,* of a certain determination is generally used to mean the difference between the analytical result x and the true value μ, i.e.

$$d = \mu - x \tag{1.1}$$

Thus the sign of the absolute error is positive if $\mu > x$ and negative if $x > \mu$: very often the error is expressed by the absolute value, without respect to the sign

$$d = |\mu - x| \tag{1.2}$$

Since the absolute error represents the difference between the result and the true value, which are both expressed in the same units, e.g. in per cent, μg/ml, etc., it has the same dimensions as they do, so that we may denote for example absolute error $d_1 = 0.005\%$ or $d_2 = 0.13\ \mu$g/ml, etc.

On adding to the value determined, the absolute error according to Eq. 1.1, we obtain the true value:

$$\mu = x + d \tag{1.3}$$

The value of the absolute error in itself, however, must be considered in conjunction with the absolute value with which it is associated. For example, an error of 0.05 % in the determination of 60 % of silica in a silicate would be regarded as satisfactory, but if it occurred in the determination of 0.01 % of arsenic in biological material the result would be quite unusable.

In many considerations, *the relative error* will serve as a criterion of the accuracy of the result:

$$e = \frac{d}{\mu} = \frac{\mu - x}{\mu} \tag{1.4}$$

This is frequently expressed in per cent, especially in analytical practice

$$e = \frac{(\mu - x)}{\mu} \times 100\% \tag{1.5}$$

but is better expressed in parts per thousand to avoid confusion with absolute errors. The correct result is obtained from the observed value and the relative error according to Eq. 1.4 by means of the relationship

$$\mu = \frac{x}{1 - e} \qquad \text{(for } e \neq 1) \tag{1.6}$$

If we know the value of e according to Eq. 1.5 we must convert it into the value of e according to Eq. 1.4 by dividing by 100, if it is to be substituted in Eq. 1.6. The relative error is not only a measure of the accuracy of the results, but by the fact that it is either a dimensionless number (Eq. 1.4) or expressed in per cent (Eq. 1.5), it permits a comparison of the accuracy of results expressed in different units.

As an example of the use of the absolute and relative error for the comparison of the accuracy of two determinations we may compare the accuracy of determination of two metals from the results: $\mu_1 = 32.6\%$; $d_1 = 0.31\%$; $\mu_2 = 7.91 \times 10^{-3}\%$; $d_2 = 0.63 \times 10^{-3}\%$.

Then $e_1 = \dfrac{0.31 \times 100}{32.6} = 0.95\,\%$, and $e_2 = \dfrac{0.63 \times 10^{-3}}{7.91 \times 10^{-3}} \times 100 = 8.0\,\%$. It is clear that the first method gave the more accurate result, because it is subject to a smaller relative error, although the absolute error was greater than in the second case.

In considering the absolute error d or the relative error e as criteria of accuracy, i.e. of the extent to which x, the result obtained, agrees with the true value μ, we must take into account that both quantities, defined by means of the value of μ, are significant only as a theoretical concept, because in practice we never know the true value μ. Equations 1.1 and 1.5 may be used only when a standard sample of known content of the component in question is being analysed in order to verify an analytical method (in this case μ is known). Sometimes, however, although we are unable to determine the absolute error precisely, we calculate the relative error by replacing the value of μ in the denominator with the value of x, or even better with the mean of several results of parallel determinations, $\bar{x}$. For the value of the absolute error in the numerator we then substitute a value determined, for example, experimentally by analysis of a standard sample, or if we wish to express the error of some measurement, we use a value estimated from various considerations such as estimation of sub-divisions on a scale. Such a relative error is then denoted, differing from the relative error according to Eq. 1.4, as

$$\varepsilon = \frac{d}{x} \qquad (1.7)$$

We shall see later that in practical work calculations of the relative error ε (sometimes expressed in per cent) are very frequent.

It must be mentioned in relation to the use of the average $\bar{x}$ instead of μ, that when we substitute the average $\bar{x}$ for the true value μ in Eq. 1.2 for the calculation of the absolute error, we obtain the deviation of the individual determination from the mean value

$$\Delta = |\,\bar{x} - x\,| \qquad (1.8)$$

Of course the deviation from the mean value includes only accidental errors, and thus it is only a criterion of the precision of individual determinations, not a measure of their accuracy. The reason is, that if all determinations are subject to a certain systematic error, their mean value is subject to the same error, and the value of Δ only involves random errors which may at most affect the precision, but not the accuracy of the results. We shall deal with the term deviation also in Chap. 4, which is concerned with mathematical statistics.

1.5 The general theory of errors

Equations 1.1, 1.4 and perhaps also 1.5, allowing a calculation of the absolute and relative error, are not sufficient for all practical cases. In practice we are concerned with the error of the final result, rather than the error of individual measurements. The calculation of the error of the final result, which we determined by means of a certain relation from values experimentally obtained, is made possible by the general theory of errors [5]. Some very important relationships for the calculation of the absolute and relative errors of some functions follow from this theory, e.g. the sum, difference, product and quotient of measured values. Although these relationships can be derived relatively simply, we shall avoid any unnecessary detail and present only the most important results in Table 1.1.

In the review shown in Table 1.1, the relationship for the error of an arbitrary function of several independent variables is perhaps the most important. According to this the absolute error is given by an expression similar to the total differential, while the relative error is equal to the absolute error of the natural logarithm of this function. However, it should be kept in mind that when calculating the relative error of some function according to the relationship in Table 1.1, we assume that all errors have the same sign and that therefore they are additive. In practice, however, errors of different signs frequently occur, that compensate each other in the final result, so that the value calculated represents a maximum value. The error may achieve this maximum value, but practically this happens only in exceptional cases. The probability of all partial errors being additive, and the extent to which they will compensate each other, will be discussed in the chapter on mathematical statistics.

Table 1.1. Calculation of the Absolute and Relative Error of Functions

---

The measured, mutually independent values $x_1, x_2, \ldots, x_n$ are subject to the absolute errors $d_{x_1}, d_{x_2}, \ldots, d_{x_n}$: the relative error of x_1 is $e_{x_1} = d_{x_1}/d_{x_2}$. The absolute error of the function y is d_y, its relative error is e_y.

General relation:

$$y = f(x_1\, x_2, \ldots, x_n) \qquad d_y = \left(\frac{\delta y}{\delta x_1}\right) d_{x_1} + \left(\frac{\delta y}{\delta x_2}\right) d_{x_2} + \ldots$$

$$e_y = \left(\frac{\delta \ln y}{\delta x_1}\right) d_{x_1} + \left(\frac{\delta \ln y}{\delta x_2}\right) d_{x_2} + \ldots$$

Sum and difference:

Absolute errors are added, the relative error is calculated from Eq. 1.4

$$y = x_1 \pm x_2 \qquad d_y = d_{x_1} + d_{x_2} \qquad e_y = \frac{d_y}{y}$$

Product with a constant:

The absolute error is multiplied by the constant, the relative error remains unchanged

$$y = a\,.\,x \qquad d_y = a\,.\,d_x \qquad e_y = e_x.$$

Product and quotient:

Relative errors are added, absolute errors are calculated from Eq. 1.4

$$y = x_1\,.\,x_2$$
$$y = \frac{x_1}{x_2} \qquad d_y = e_y\,.\,y \qquad e_y = e_{x_1} + e_{x_2}$$

Powers and roots:

The relative error is multiplied by the exponent

$$y = x^n \qquad d_y = n\,.\,x^{n-1}\,.\,d_x \qquad e_y = n\,.\,e_x$$

The practical importance of the general theory of errors does not lie in the calculation of errors, but in the search for ideal conditions, under which the error of the result will be minimum. Let us only indicate the procedure: it is known from mathematics, that a function achieves a minimum for those values of the independent variable for which the first derivatives with respect to all variables are equal to zero (necessary condition). We therefore find the first order partial derivatives for all possible variables of the error calculation function, equate them to zero and calculate from them the values of all the variables. At first sight this certainly is a tempting solution, although sometimes it is rather a difficult mathematical problem. Besides, we rarely encounter in practice such a relation between several variables, which could be expressed by a simple mathematical function of several variables. In practice the situation is, moreover, complicated by the fact that a minimum determined by mathematical means need not have any physical significance. Thus a practical result is obtained in isolated cases only. Furthermore the possibilities of measurement errors caused by the instruments used are not taken into consideration in the calculation. Thus the results of such calculations must always be amplified by a logical consideration, and especially they must be verified experimentally. Some cases of the determination of the most favourable conditions of measurement with regard to analytical practice will be given in the following chapters.

1.6 Relative error of the final result of a chemical analysis

In carrying out a chemical analysis, either by an absolute chemical method or a comparative physico-chemical method, the procedure invariably involves weighing a certain amount of the sample, which we shall denote x_1. With this weighed sample we then perform the entire analytical procedure, obtaining a certain value which is proportional to the amount of the particular component determined in the sample. We shall denote this value x_2. The result of the analysis is then given, in the case of an absolute method, by the relationship

$$p = k \cdot \frac{x_2}{x_1} \tag{1.9}$$

This value is expressed as a per cent or as a concentration (e.g. in mg/ml): k is a constant expressing the proportionality between the value measured and the actual amount or concentration of the component required. Sometimes, however, this k does not represent a true constant, but also includes a value determined experimentally, e.g. the titre of a volumetric solution, x_3, so that

$$p = x_3 \cdot k' \frac{x_2}{x_1} \tag{1.10}$$

The relative maximum error of the final result ε_p is then given by the relation

$$\varepsilon_p = \varepsilon_{x_1} + \varepsilon_{x_2} + \varepsilon_{x_3} = \sum_1^j \varepsilon_{x_j} \tag{1.11}$$

which follows from the general theory of error. The symbol $\sum_{1}^{j} \varepsilon_{x_j}$ denotes the sum of relative errors of all values experimentally determined and so subject to error. Assuming the validity of Eq. 1.9, i.e. if k is the conversion factor for a gravimetric determination, calculated from atomic weights, j will be equal to 2 in Eq. 1.11 because the precision of the determination of atomic weights is so high that the value of ε_{x_3} is negligible compared with that of ε_{x_1} and ε_{x_2}. We therefore add only ε_{x_1} and ε_{x_2}: if $k = x_3 \cdot k'$, where x_3 from Eq. 1.10 is, for example, the titre of a volumetric solution and k' is the equivalent, we obtain $j = 3$: then we cannot neglect the error of determination of the factor and we add ε_{x_1}, ε_{x_2} and ε_{x_3}. In the case of comparative methods we use an entire functional relation, determined experimentally, instead of a single value of x_3. Such an experimental determination of a functional relation is generally carried out by establishing the dependence of the measured value on the concentration of the component in question, and we generally treat the results from a number of experiments graphically. We must then consider the relation

$$p = \frac{1}{x_1} \cdot f(x_2) \qquad (1.12)$$

If we find that the function $f(x_2)$ is linear, at least over a certain concentration range, we may again replace the entire functional relation with the expression $x_3 \cdot k' x_2$ and comparison with a single standard suffices, for example in the procedure known under the name "standard addition method". It is evident that the accuracy of the final result will then depend not only on the error of determining the measured value in the analysis of the sample, but also on errors which accompany the determination of the dependence of the measured value on the concentration of the component to be determined, i.e. the errors of determining the proportionality constant k', or the entire functional relation $f(x_2)$.

The important point in our discussion is the result which follows from Eq. 1.11 and from the statements above, i.e. the fact that the relative error of the result of chemical analysis is equal to the sum of relative errors of all values which are determined experimentally and used to calculate the analytical result. This, of course, does not mean that the actual relative error always attains this value, but rather that in an extreme case it may attain values up to the sum of relative errors of all measurements. In actual fact positive as well as negative errors could occur in general and compensate each other [57].

1.7 Errors of procedure and errors of measurement

Let us now turn to the individual values x_1, x_2 and x_3, and let us note the way in which we determine their value. The sample weight x_1 is generally set down in the analytical procedure. We know the value of this weight with such precision as we achieve in the weighing process, and in its determination no other errors are involved save the error of weighing. On the other hand, when x_2 is being determined, we must consider the error of the measurement by means of which the value of x_2 is being determined, e.g. the error involved in reading on a burette the consumption of a volumetric solution, reading an absorbance value, determining the height of a polarographic wave etc., as well as all errors arising in performing the analytical procedure, e.g. partial solubility of a precipitate, titration with an indicator which does not indicate the end-point exactly at the point of equivalence (the so-called error of titration), source oscillations in emission spectrography etc.

We know from practice that these errors of procedure are frequently greater than the errors of measurement and that they are the main factors which influence the accuracy of the final result, especially in the analysis of more complicated samples where various separation processes are necessary.

The value of the factor x_3 is usually determined as the ratio of an assumed and an observed value: this ratio is usually obtained with relatively great precision as the mean of several determinations which, moreover, are in themselves subject only to small errors of accidental character. For this reason the relative error of the titre ε_{x_3} is frequently negligible in comparison to ε_{x_1} and especially to ε_{x_2}, so that Eq. 1.10 may sometimes be replaced by Eq. 1.9 even in the case of a titre which is determined experimentally. On the other hand, with physico-chemical methods which generally involve comparison with a standard, the value of the error ε_{x_3} also includes the purity of the standard employed and the errors in determining the functional relation $f(x_2)$, so that we generally also have to take the error ε_{x_3} into consideration. A typical example, where the accuracy of determining the relation $f(x_2)$ is decisive for the analytical result, is spectrographic analysis by means of the internal standard method [1, 67].

It may be stated in general that with chemical methods the error of the final result is in most cases given, in principle, by the error involved in the determination of the value of x_2, i.e. the magnitude of ε_{x_2}. The reason is, that this value already includes the errors of the entire analytical procedure which must be carried out in order to determine the value of x_2.

On the other hand, with physico-chemical or purely physical methods of analysis, the maximum relative error is mainly given by the sum $(\varepsilon_{x_2} + \varepsilon_{x_3})$, i.e. the sum of the error of the measurement proper and the error of determining the relation between the quantity measured and the concentration of the component analysed.

1.8 Influence of the precision of measurement and of the absolute value of the quantity measured, on the relative error

We have spoken in the preceding paragraph about the influence of the relative errors of the determination of x_1, x_2 and x_3 on the relative error of the final result. Now let us investigate the factors which influence the magnitude of such relative error.

It can be seen from Eq. 1.4 that the magnitude of the relative error is determined by the absolute error of the determination and by the absolute value of the quantity determined, and that thus the relative error is the smaller (i) the smaller the absolute error d, (ii) the greater the absolute magnitude of the value of the quantity determined x, or theoretically, of the true value μ.

When we wish to achieve final results subject to the least possible relative error, we must not only avoid the formation of large absolute errors in determining the values of x_1 and especially of x_2, and possibly also errors in the determination of x_3, but the whole procedure must be selected in such a way that the values of x_1 and x_2 should not be too small with regard to the precision with which they are being determined. An excessively small value of x_2 is — beside the risk of contamination — the main reason for the relatively poor precision of the results of trace analyses. For practical reasons, of course, the sample weight x_1 cannot be increased at will, and therefore the value of x_2 also remains within certain limits. It is true that in this way it would be possible to decrease the relative error of measurement of x_1 and x_2, but the experimental difficulties involved for example in handling large amounts of precipitates, the impossibility of thoroughly washing such precipitates, or difficulties with large solution volumes etc. would lead to such procedural errors that the final result would in the end be less precise and accurate than if we worked with smaller sample amounts even at the price of a somewhat greater relative error of measurement. On the contrary, modern analytical chemistry continues to convert to semi-micro- and microanalytical procedures because of their undoubted advantages. The use of such procedures of course requires that the determination be carried out with an absolute error which is proportionately small with respect to the amounts with which we are working.

Thus, for example, when 0.50 g is weighed with a precision of ± 0.2 mg the relative error is $\varepsilon = \dfrac{0.2 \times 100}{500} = 0.04\,\%$; if we are to weigh only 25 mg with the same relative error, we must weigh with an absolute error d, which may be calculated from the relation $0.04 = \dfrac{d \times 100}{25}$, i.e. a precision of ± 0.01 mg. Thus it is clear that precise weighing with the precision of $\pm$ 0.01 mg necessitates not only special equipment, but also much greater care in the weighing operation. On the other hand it is quite pointless to weigh a sample of e.g. 2 g with a precision better than ± 0.2 mg, because the relative error is in this case so small that it has no practical influence anyway on the error of the final result, in comparison with the other errors of procedure and measurement.

In the case of some physico-chemical methods (e.g. in polarography) the relative error depends only to a small degree on the absolute concentration of the component analysed. Evidently methods of this type are specially suitable for the determination of small concentrations of components, e.g. trace elements.

In general the problem of decreasing the relative error of the final result should be solved rather by more precise measurement of x_1 and x_2 than by increasing their absolute value. Especially should this be done by eliminating the errors of procedure, which influence the absolute error of the determination of the quality x_2. The influence of the absolute values of x_1 or x_2 and x_3 on the relative error of the result can become effective only in special cases, e.g. the determination of slight traces of a certain element. In such a case, of course, it is essential either to choose a large sample weight and concentrate the component to be analysed, before the final measurement of the value of x_2, or to employ a method of such sensitivity as to make the value of x_2 sufficiently large even for a low concentration of the component in question.

1.9 The influence of the constant k on the error of the result

The value of the constant k from Eq. 1.9 determines, for a given value of p, the relationship between x_1 and x_2 insofar as the magnitude of x_2 depends, for a certain p, on the magnitude of the sample weight x_1. Since the absolute values of x_1 and x_2 also influence the error of the final result, the value of k is also not unimportant for the error of the final result. Moreover the value of k from Eq. 1.9 or the slope of the function $f(x_2)$ from Eq. 1.12 are measures of the sensitivity of the analytical method, i.e. of the variation of the quantity measured with variations of the concentration of the respective component. The smaller the value of k, the more sensitive is the method and thus also the smaller is the absolute error of measurement.

When, for example, we are weighing ignited aluminium oxide in the determination of aluminium (factor $f_1 = 0.529$) and our error of weighing is 0.2 mg, the absolute error of the determination of aluminium will be $d_1 = 0.529 \times 0.2 = 0.106$ mg of Al. When, however, we are weighing aluminium oxinate instead (factor $f_2 = 0.0578$) the absolute error of the determination of aluminium is only $d_2 = 0.0578 \times 0.2 = 0.012$ mg of Al. Moreover the analysis is more sensitive in this latter case: for 1 mg of Al we weigh 1.88 mg of aluminium oxide or 17.1 mg of aluminium oxinate. The statement would thus appear to be justified, that the more sensitive method, i.e. the method with the smaller factor, is always the more advantageous for the determination. Let us, however, study the overall error of the analytical result. If we are to determine 1 % of Al by means of the ammonia method, we obtain 0.0189 g of Al_2O_3 from a sample of 1 g. When weighing by the differential method, i.e. determining the sample weight and weight of the final compound as the differences of two weighings with a precision of ± 0.2 mg each, the error may, according to Eq. 1.11, achieve a value of up to $\varepsilon = \dfrac{2 \times 0.2 \times 100}{1000} + \dfrac{2 \times 0.2 \times 100}{18.9} = 2.15\,\%$.

By precipitating aluminium with oxine, however, i.e. employing the method having the lower factor, we weigh from a sample of 0.60 g some 0.104 g of oxinate, so that the maximum error of the result decreases to $\varepsilon = \dfrac{2 \times 0.2 \times 100}{600} + \dfrac{2 \times 0.2 \times 100}{104} = 0.45\,\%$.

On the other hand, when analysing a sample containing 60 % Al, we must weigh a sample of 0.176 g in order to obtain 0.20 g of aluminium oxide, and thus $\varepsilon = \dfrac{2 \times 0.2 \times 100}{176} + \dfrac{2 \times 0.2 \times 100}{200} = 0.43\,\%$, but when using the oxinate method we may take a sample of only 19.3 mg in order not to obtain more than 200 mg of aluminium oxinate; now the maximum error of the entire determination will be $\varepsilon = \dfrac{2 \times 0.2 \times 100}{19.3} + \dfrac{2 \times 0.2 \times 100}{200} = 2.27\,\%$.

It is to be seen from this example that more sensitive methods are suitable for the determination of small contents (a small amount of the component analysed corresponds to a large value of x_2), while a method of lower sensitivity will give reliable results only when used to determine greater concentrations, in which case, on the contrary, a method of too large a sensitivity would be unsuitable (a very small sample would have to be weighed, or a stock solution would have to be made and an aliquot measured by pipette). At the same time the example illustrates a well known experience from practical analysis, i.e. that one and the same method, suitable e.g. for a low content of the respective component, may be quite unsuitable for the determination of a large content. In the calculations of the maximum relative error in the manner described, possible errors of procedure are, of course, not taken into consideration.

1.10 The origin of random, systematic and gross errors

Let us now investigate the principal difference between *errors of measurement* and *errors of procedure*, as discussed in section 1.7.

Errors of measurement are generally of random character, while the origin of errors of procedure may sometimes also involve influences which lead to systematic errors. Of course, even errors such as the error of weighing (i.e. an error of measurement) may attain systematic character to a certain extent, e.g. this may happen in cases where a stock solution is prepared and aliquots are measured by pipette for individual determinations. All analytical results are then distorted by the same error in the same sense. On the other hand it should be kept in mind, that an accidental error of weighing (e.g. $\pm$ 0.2 mg) is decreased to such an extent by taking aliquots, that it is hardly noticeable in the final result. Thus, while leaving out of consideration the possibility of a gross error in the measurement proper, we may state that the sources of systematic errors are exclusively *errors of procedure* (and also, of course, imperfections of volumetric glassware and instruments, impurities in reagents, etc.). Gross errors caused by the analyst may consist either in the measurement proper, or in some operation of the analytical procedure: this circumstance, of course, cannot be established afterwards, other than errors of calculation.

When discussing the origin of systematic, random and gross errors, it should also be noted that sometimes one and the same cause, which under some circumstances leads to the origin of a systematic error, may under other conditions cause only a decrease of the precision of parallel results. Sometimes it is also too difficult to decide when an error is to be regarded as a random error and when it has already become a gross error. The criterion of the occurrence of a gross error is generally taken to be a rather large difference from other results: with some methods, of course, the differences between parallel determinations are relatively large (low reproducibility of the method), although these differences cannot be explained by the occurrence of gross errors.

Thus in practice we usually assume a small error appearing irregularly to be a random error, an error appearing regularly is taken as a systematic error and an unduly large error appearing individually is taken to be a gross error, remembering all the while that in principle there is a continuous transition between random, systematic and gross errors. As we shall see later, the problem of distinguishing between random, systematic and gross errors is solved far more perfectly in mathematical statistics, where the mathematically expressed concept of probability is used, e.g. the probability that a certain limiting magnitude of a deviation will be achieved, or the probability of occurrence of an error of a certain sign in relation to the overall number of all results.

1.11 The reliability and reproducibility of the results of chemical analyses

When assessing a certain analytical method, we are generally interested most in learning whether a method, which is conventionally employed to check a certain material, is sufficiently reliable, i.e. to what extent its results are accurate or how far they agree with the actual content of the component analysed. Furthermore we wish to know whether roughly the same accuracy is achieved in the analyses of different samples, or whether the accuracy of the results obtained by means of this method varies with a small change of the overall composition of the samples, or even whether the accuracy of this method varies for undetectable reasons; sometimes the agreement of parallel determinations need not vary with varying accuracy.

The accuracy of the results of a given analysis can never be safely guaranteed; we may only judge the accuracy by experimentally verifying our method by means of the analysis of a substance of precisely known composition, or of a standard sample, the composition of which is approximately the same as that of the analytical sample, comparing the results obtained with the actual content of the component analysed in the standard sample. If a standard sample is not available, a synthetic mixture of the same composition as the sample analysesd will suffice in most cases. The accuracy of equipment, i.e. balances, instruments, calibration of glassware etc. also should be checked periodically. Realization of a total of 100% for the sum of all results is sometimes used as a criterion of accuracy of a complete analysis: e.g. for complete analysis, HILLEBRAND [16] states a range of 99.95 to 100.08% for simple alloys and 99.75 to 100.50% for minerals. Systematic errors originating in the separation of individual components, however, need not necessarily affect the sum of results, since a proportion of one component will "pass through" and be determined with another component. Thus the agreement of the sum of all results of a complete analysis may be taken either as proof of the accuracy of all results, or as proof of the perfect compensation of the errors of determination of the individual components of the sample. If the agreement is a case of compensation only, however, the extent to which the sum of results agrees with 100% will vary from case to case, as it is difficult to assume equally perfect compensation in every analysis. In analyses of salts, e.g. of mineral waters, the equality of the sums of cations and anions may be taken as a measure of accuracy.

Another property which an analyst studies in a conventional method is the reproducibility of its results, i.e. the stability of precision or mutual agreement of parallel results with slight variations of the sample composition. If the composition of the samples varies substantially, precision usually varies also; this variation of precision with the varying content of the component analysed should, however, be regular. If the demand of reproducibility is satisfied, an outstanding deviation from the usual degree of precision may be a sign of the fact that one of the parallel determinations may be distorted by a gross error. For this reason it is important in practice to know the value of the permissible difference of parallel determinations, which may be established numerically in a very simple and relatively reliable way, using mathematical statistics. It may happen sometimes, that with results obtained by means of a certain analytical method, different agreement of parallel results occurs, without the possibility of explaining the difference by a gross error. If such a striking variability of the agreement of results is noted, i.e. an inferior reliability, it must always be considered whether the analytical procedure is really suitable for the given type of material analysed, and whether it should be attempted to eliminate these variations by a modification of the analytical procedure.

1.12 Elimination of the influence of errors of chemical analyses

It has been shown in the preceding sections how the origin of random and gross errors may be explained, and that systematic errors are mainly caused by errors of procedure. We have furthermore seen that the difference between accidental and rough errors mainly consists in their magnitude and that the difference between accidental and systematic errors mainly consists in the stability of the sense and magnitude of the error (see Figs. 1a, b).

The most important question which we shall now discuss is the limitation of the occurrence of errors in chemical analyses to the lowest possible level, and possibly the determination of their influence on the final result. With respect to the variegated causes of occurrence of the individual kinds of errors, and also with respect to the fact that the final error of a determination frequently also includes e.g. random errors of measurement and procedure together with a definite though very small systematic error inherent in the procedure, it is clear that no universal recipe can be given for eliminating all errors, but that a solution must be sought for every individual case.

Errors of prevailingly systematic character are usually inherent in the procedure, and therefore they are best eliminated by modifying the experimental conditions. The question of where the causes of systematic errors should be looked for, is discussed in Chap. 3 which deals with this aspect of analytical methods. Even in those cases where the errors of measurement have no major effect on the final result compared to errors of procedure, it is desirable to limit even these insubstantial errors to a minimum. The possibilities of decreasing the error of measurement to the lowest possible extent will be discussed in Chap. 2. In cases where the errors in question will mainly be random, and especially in cases where it is necessary to decide whether it is only an accidental error or a systematic or gross one, the methods of mathematical statistics described in Chap. 4 may be used with success.

Although the assessment of analytical methods based on the precision and accuracy of the results is of first-rate importance, and in fact the major part of this book is devoted to it, it should yet be noted that besides the assessment of the numerical values of the results we must also consider the technical detail of obtaining the results, i.e. the demands on time, difficulties of performance of the overall analytical procedure, and the costs involved in the individual analytical methods. Moreover, the precision of results of a given analytical method is often indirectly correlated to the ease of performance of the method, because with a complicated and lengthy procedure there always is a greater possibility for the occurrence of the most variegated errors of procedure. The speed and ease of performance, and also of course the frequently very high sensitivity of physico-chemical methods are the reasons why these methods replace the exact, often very precise, but lengthy classical methods to an increasing degree in practical analytical chemistry.

The correct choice of a suitable analytical procedure is very important for the final results of the analysis, but it is not sufficient in itself; without care in carrying out the procedure we cannot regard our results as reliable. For this reason the problem of reliability of analytical results cannot be taken as a purely technical problem; to a large extent it is also a problem of the training and experience of the analyst: very much also depends on the organization of work within an analytical laboratory.

Chapter 2

MEASUREMENTS USED
IN CHEMICAL ANALYSES

2.1 Weighing

Weighing is the most basic and most important operation in chemical analysis. It is, in principle, a comparative method, in which we compare the mass of the object weighed with the mass of weights, using balances.

In practice the following two types of analytical balances are most frequently used.

1. On *undamped balances* we counterpoise the object with weights of the same mass, first by placing weights on the other pan of the balance and finally by adding milligrams and tenths of milligrams with a rider. Alternatively we can measure the final small difference in mass between the loads on the pans by measuring the deflection of the beam from the horizontal, when the beam is at rest. A disadvantage of this older type of balance is that the sensitivity of the balance varies with the load. It is often claimed that the time needed for a weighing is unduly long and is a disadvantage, especially in routine analyses, but this is not always so if the operator is really skilled. The error of weighing with such balances, if all rules are adhered to as usually described in text-books of analytical chemistry, is generally ± 0.2 mg for the overall weighing operation.

2. More modern types of balances are generally *damped (aperiodic)*, permitting more rapid weighing, especially by unskilled operators. Gram and fractional weights are usually added mechanically as ring-riders on a carrier-bar at one end of the balance beam; milligrams and their fractions are read on a projected image of a scale attached to the pointer of the balance. A vernier is sometimes fitted to the scale projection. The error of weighing is usually the same as with non-damped balances, i.e. about ± 0.2 mg. With the more sensitive balances known as semi-microbalances and microbalances, a rider is used to add milligrams and the scale can be read to 1 or 10 micrograms.

Besides these types of balance, there are *microbalances* based on a different principle: there are torsion balances (the force compensating the weight of the object is created by twisting a fibre), spring balances, and electromagnetic balances with the possibility of remote control suitable for work with radioisotopes. Such microbalances (often called ultramicrobalances) make it possible to weigh microgram to milligram amounts, with an absolute error of only a tenth of a microgram, or less.

Let us investigate the problem of *weighing on analytical balances and semi-microbalances*. It is demanded of good balances that they must be accurate and precise, i.e. on repeated weighing we must always obtain the same results, the average of which is the true weight. Moreover, after weighing, the balances should return exactly to the "zero position" and they should react even to small weight changes, i.e. be sufficiently sensitive. With non-damped balances it is moreover very important that they have a short oscillation period (around 10 seconds), while damped balances should not be over-damped (they would take too long to come to rest) but should be really aperiodic (very few oscillations before coming to rest). Sensitivity and oscillation period influence the precision of balances to a certain extent, depending on the length of the balance beam and position of the centre of gravity, which with some types of balance may be varied within certain limits. On the other hand, the accuracy of balances depends primarily on the design of the beam, which should not bend when loaded. The weight of the beam is also of significance. For this reason beams are used which are of lattice construction but resist bending. Most importantly, all three knives must lie in one plane and be mutually parallel; the two arms should be of equal length.

A slight difference in the arm-lengths need not be taken into account if we are concerned with relative weighing and always place the object on the same (e.g. left-hand) pan, the weights being placed on the other pan.

The sensitivity of balances, i.e. the deflection expressed in scale divisions per milligram difference between load on the pans, varies with the load of the balance, being greatest with the balance unloaded. In the case of non-damped balances this circumstance is of no great significance; at most it influences to a certain extent the reproducibility of weighing. It is, however, very important in aperiodic balances that it should be eliminated as far as possible by proper design of the balance. In most aperiodic balances [36] of two-pan design, the variation of sensitivity with load is practically constant over the working range. In one-pan substitution-type balances, which operate at constant load, the problem does not arise. It can cause difficulty in undamped balances (usually free-swinging microbalances) in which the deflection of the beam is determined by means of projection of the image of a graticule on the pointer. This error will be most serious when we are reading at the end of the scale.

Since the error of weight readings, caused by lower sensitivity, increases with the absolute magnitude of the deflection, we try when weighing relatively heavy objects to read always in that half of the scale which is closer to zero. Better than to read at the end of the positive scale is to add an increment of weight, read the negative deflection and subtract. Because in this way we usually obtain a final value which is too big, while when reading on the positive scale the value is too low, it may be recommended to read first on the positive, then on the negative scale, and to take a mean of the two values. A frequent source of gross errors is wrong suspension of the ring-riders or placing weights at the edge of the pan, so that the pan axis deviates from the perpendicular position or the pans start to swing, etc.

In analytical practice, weighing by difference is used practically exclusively. As both weighings are carried out with the same vessel no correction for air buoyancy is needed. The correct weighing procedure, as described in most text-books of analytical chemistry, is of course essential for obtaining accurate results when weighing. Great care must be taken of balances, e.g. correct placing to protect them from corrosive atmospheres, and protection from shock and vibration. It is also essential to protect the balances from unsymmetrical heating, e.g. by radiators or lamps. Details will be found in the specialized literature [36].

For accurate weighing, the accuracy or precision of the weights used is as important as the accuracy and precision of the balance. Weights are supplied in sets with analytical balances. For precise weighing there must be mutual (relative) agreement of the individual weights of one set (i.e. precision): e.g. two 1-gram weights must have the same weight as one 2-gram weight, etc. For weighing by difference, which is most frequent in analytical practice, this condition is even more important than exact absolute agreement of the masses of individual weights with their nominal value. The accuracy or precision of individual weights may be established by means of calibration; in principle every new set of weights should be calibrated, and weights which have been in use for some time should be checked.

2.2 Calibration of analytical weights

We shall describe here calibration by the substitution method according to RICHARDS. This method is relatively simple, the influence of non-equality of balance beam arms is eliminated, and the method is suitable for all conventional types of analytical weight sets, whether they be composed according to the scheme 1, 1, 2, 5 or 1, 2, 2, 5 or 1, 2, 3, 5 for the relative values of the weights. The determination of relative corrections allows calibrated weight sets to be used in all cases where the calculation of the result is based on the ratio of two weights (i.e. in the majority of analytical procedures); only in quite exceptional cases, when it is required that the set be accurate (not merely precise), must we include an absolute standard in the set of weights. When calibrating to determine the precision of our set, we need an auxiliary set of weights as tare, as well as auxiliary weights of 0.01 g, 0.1 g and 10 g. We place a 5-mg weight on the left-hand pan of the balance, leaving this weight on the pan during the entire calibration in order that the left-hand pan should always be the heavier.

We start by calibrating the smallest weight: we place a weight of 0.01 g (which we are going to assume as accurate) on the left-hand pan, tare with the same weight from the auxiliary set and compensate with the rider or read the scale deflection. Because of the 5-mg tare on the left-hand pan, the deflection or rider-position will correspond approximately to 5 mg. We note this value, replace the weight with another 10-mg weight from the set being calibrated and repeat the process: if we find a different deflection (or rider position) we add or subtract this difference as correction of this weight. We then put on the left-hand pan the two 10-mg fractions, tare them with a 0.02-g fraction from the auxiliary set, determine the deflection or rider position in equilibrium and replace the two 10-mg fractions with a 0.02-g weight from the calibrated set. We thus proceed further.

Because we chose the smallest weight as temporary reference weight, we sometimes observe rather large deviations from the nominal value in the case of the larger weights. Calculations with large corrections would be unwieldy, and therefore for a final reference weight we select one of the larger weights, e.g. the 20-g, the weight of which we assume to be accurate and therefore identical with the nominal value, and we calculate the corrections of the other weights on this basis. In practice, when several weights are always used together for weighing, the final correction is equal to the algebraic sum of the corrections of all weights used. For speed it is of advantage to make a table of all possible combinations of individual corrections: the smallest number of weights should always be used when weighing, and if the set includes several weights of the same nominal value, these must be marked to distinguish them and they must be used in the order indicated by the correction table. Other calibration methods for weights have been described by LÜPKE [76]. Table 2.1 lists permissible deviations for individual weights.

Of course, the weighing operations carried out when calibrating sets of weights, are subject to random errors, a fact which influences the accuracy of the entire calibration. CHALMERS and CURNOW [44] have shown that the influence of random errors of weighing in the course of calibration may be limited to a substantial degree, by repeating the individual weighing operations, by using several different standards to calibrate each single set of weights and especially by weighing different combinations of weights against each other and, in particular, by including some weights in which there are more than one weight in both pans.

Table 2.1. Accuracy of Weights

Nominal weight g	Permissible deviation mg	Nominal weight mg	Permissible deviation mg
500	3	500	0.05
200	1	200	0.05
100	0.5	100	0.05
50	0.3	50	0.03
20	0.2	20	0.03
10	0.15	10	0.02
5	0.15	5	0.02
2	0.10	2	0.01
1	0.10	1	0.01

2.3 The relative error of weighing

The relative error of an individual weighing is given by Eqs. 1.4 or 1.5: it depends on the one hand on the absolute precision of weighing, expressed in this case by the absolute error d, and on the other hand on the mass of the object weighed. The absolute precision of weighing is, of course, influenced by the sensitivity of the balance, which may vary with the load, i.e. the weight of the object weighted, in which case the error of weighing is mainly influenced by the mass of the object weighed (beside other influences due to the design of the balances, accuracy of weights etc.). The mass of the object should not be too small, as otherwise the value of the relative error according to Eq. 1.4 might become too large, but the balance should not be loaded too much, in order that the sensitivity should not decrease unnecessarily.

The problem of the most suitable mass for individual weighing operations and a given balance can be solved very simply by consideration of the sensitivity of the balance and calculation of the relative error. In a weighing by difference let the mass of the container and the substance weighed be x_a, and of the container alone, x_b: then the mass x of the substance weighed is $x_a - x_b$. Thus the precision of the differential weighing is influenced not only by the weight of the substance, but also by the weight of the vessel. To determine the relative error of x we must use the relationship for the relative maximum error of a difference (p. 12) i.e.

$$\varepsilon = \frac{d_{x_a} + d_{x_b}}{x_a - x_b}. \tag{2.1}$$

Since the absolute error of weighing depends on the sensitivity of the balance, then if this decreases approximately linearly with the load, we may consider the absolute error of weighing to be approximately

$$d_{x_a} = k \cdot x_a, \qquad d_{x_b} = k \cdot x_b \tag{2.2}$$

where k should be as small as possible. The relative errors of weighing a weighing bottle with sample and without are

$$\varepsilon_a = \frac{d_{x_a}}{x_a} = \frac{d_{x_a}}{x_a} \cdot 100\% \quad \text{and} \quad \varepsilon_b = \frac{d_{x_b}}{x_b} = \frac{d_{x_b}}{x_b} \cdot 100\%. \tag{2.3}$$

The relative error of the differential weighing is

$$\varepsilon_x = \frac{k(x_a + x_b)}{x_a - x_b}. \tag{2.4}$$

Let us now investigate this relation more closely, and attempt to establish the conditions under which the error ε_x will be least. In order that the right-hand side of the equation (2.4) should be small, the difference $x_a - x_b$ must be large and the sum $x_a + x_b$ must be small.

The difference $x_a - x_b$ is large if $x_a \gg x_b$, but at the same time the absolute value of x_b must be small in order that the sum $x_a + x_b$ should also be small. This means that the vessel used for weighing should itself be light (small value of x_b) and the mass of the substance weighed ($x = x_a - x_b$) should not be too small.

Let us now calculate the smallest mass which may be weighed in order that in differential weighing the error should not be greater than say 0.1%. Assuming that $d_{x_a} = d_{x_b}$ for small values of x, conventional analytical balances ($d = 0.2$ mg) should not be used to weigh masses smaller than $x = \dfrac{2 \times 0.2 \times 100}{0.1} = 400$ mg, while in the case of semi-microbalances ($d = 0.02$ mg) masses weighed should not be less than $x = \dfrac{2 \times 0.2 \times 100}{0.1} = 40$ mg. In practice, of course, we sometimes determine masses of less than 0.4 mg with analytical balances: in such a case, if no other procedure can be used, we must be aware of the possibility of a larger weighing error even if all the rules of correct weighing are satisfied. It is sometimes possible, as will be shown later, to decrease the error in the sample weight by preparing a stock solution and taking aliquots by pipette.

Let us now consider the influence of the weight of the container used. An investigation of the sensitivity of single-pan Meopta Type A3 balances has shown that the absolute error of weighing up to loads of roughly 25 g is $d = 0.2$ mg; with loads of 50 g this value rises to $d = 0.5$ mg. If we weigh 0.2 g in a 12-g boat the relative error of weighing is $\varepsilon_1 = \dfrac{2 \times 0.2 \times 100}{12\,200 - 12\,000} = 0.20\%$, but if we use a 50-g weighing bottle, we have $\varepsilon_2 = \dfrac{2 \times 0.5 \times 100}{50\,200 - 50\,000} = 0.50\%$: thus the error of the entire weighing operation increases substantially, simply due to the use of an unduly heavy weighing vessel on a balance which does not have a constant sensitivity. In this way we may at least roughly determine the conditions of weighing with Meopta A3 balances, if it is required that the relative weighing error is always to be less than some predetermined value [56].

2.4 Influence of humidity and temperature on the accuracy of weighing

When weighing vessels of glass, porcelain or silica, especially if these have a large surface, we must taken into account a certain error caused by water adsorption on the vessel surface. The amount of moisture adsorbed on the surface of objects, especially glassware, depends on a great variety of conditions, e.g. atmospheric humidity, temperature, pressure, etc. When we attempt to obtain a reproducible moisture film on objects by wiping them with a cloth and then letting them stand in the balance case atmosphere, the objects may become electrified. Therefore a glass object should, after wiping, be left inside the balance cabinet long enough to allow it to lose its electrical charge, or it can be earthed or passed through a flame or treated with ionizing radiation. A difference in temperature between the object weighed and the balance may also be a source of considerable error: some authors mention an error of roughly 0.15 mg for 1 °C temperature difference between the object and the balance [37, 41].

These errors are sometimes rather difficult to overcome in a single weighing operation. Luckily, in analytical practice weighing procedures other than the differential one are seldom used, and thus it suffices to maintain absolutely the same procedure in both weighings, thus achieving approximately the same weight variations due to humidity, temperature or air buoyancy differences for the weights and the object weighed. However, this procedure should be selected in such a way as to achieve "equilibrium" of the individual influences and in order that the mass of the object weighed should not vary with weighing conditions. Such a correct weighing procedure, which follows not only from logical considerations but which has also been verified in practice in countless cases, is described in every textbook of quantitative analytical chemistry or of practical physics, and it must always be carefully adhered to, even in routine analyses.

2.5 Measuring solutions

Correct measuring of solution volumes and their dilution to a given volume are of equal importance to correct weighing in analytical chemistry.

Measuring of approximate volumes of auxiliary solutions, where the amount added is not critical, is most often done by means of measuring cylinders. In such cases small deviations of measuring do not cause errors large enough to influence the final result, but if the error of measuring is large enough to cause, for example, addition of an insufficient amount of precipitating agent, the final result will, of course, be subject to a gross error.

The final result is influenced to a much larger extent, for example, by the determination of the consumption of a titrant, making up the sample solution to a certain volume, taking aliquots, etc. Here every error will affect the final result, and owing to their differing magnitude such errors may take the character of "elementary errors", which together with other "elementary errors" will be added or compensated to give the random error of the analysis: if such errors are larger in magnitude, however, they may attain the character of gross errors, and in some cases, e.g. in taking aliquots by pipette for parallel analyses, such errors may even become systematic to a certain degree.

The first prerequisite of correct measurement and making up of solutions is satisfactory glassware. There are two types of volumetric glassware: that used to make up solutions to a given volume, and calibrated to "contain", e.g. volumetric flasks, and that for measuring solutions (e.g. pipettes, burettes) which are calibrated to "deliver", their volume being larger by the amount which adheres to the vessel walls. Piston burettes, e.g. the "Agla" micrometer syringe, are found to be useful in carrying out microanalyses.

In each case the glassware must be perfectly clean and degreased, e.g. by chromic acid or a permanganate-sulphuric acid mixture, washed with distilled water and treated with silicones if thought necessary. The quickest way of cleaning dry glassware is to rinse it successively with small volumes of benzene and concentrated sulphuric acid, and then to wash it well with water. Silicone tap-grease should never be used. If glassware is used at a temperature differing from the one for which it was calibrated, corrections should be applied.

2.6 Calibration of glassware

The following circumstances must be taken into consideration in the determination of the true volume of a glass vessel.

1. The density of water depends on temperature, so that one litre of water does not weigh 1 000 g at all temperatures; the water density for different temperatures is given in Table 2.2.

2. Owing to air buoyancy, which at a given temperature depends on the barometric pressure, a vessel of large volume will weigh less than if it were weighed in a vacuum, and a correction should be applied.

3. The volume of a glass vessel varies with temperature.

To determine the true volume of a vessel calibrated "to contain", we weigh it, fill it with water up to the mark and weigh again; the weight of water used, multiplied by the factor given in Table 2.2, gives the true volume for the given temperature. Vessels calibrated "to deliver" are checked by weighing the water actually delivered when they are emptied by a standard

Table 2.2. Density of Water d_{H_2O} and $f = \dfrac{1}{d_{H_2O}}$ at Different
Temperatures and Calibration of Volumetric Glassware

$t\ °C$	d_{H_2O}	$\log d$	f	$\log f$
15.0	0.999126	9996203	1.001955	0.0008480
15.5	0.999050	9995872	1.002028	0.0008799
16.0	0.998970	9995524	1.002107	0.0009140
16.5	0.998887	9995164	1.002188	0.0009493
17.0	0.998801	9994789	1.002273	0.0009860
17.5	0.998713	9994407	1.002359	0.0010232
18.0	0.998622	9994012	1.002448	0.0010620
18.5	0.998528	9993603	1.002541	0.0011022
19.0	0.998432	9993185	1.002636	0.0011433
19.5	0.998332	9992750	1.002735	0.0011860
20.0	0.998230	9992306	1.002835	0.0012294
20.5	0.998126	9991854	1.002937	0.0012738
21.0	0.998019	9991388	1.003043	0.0013197
21.5	0.997909	9990910	1.003152	0.0013669
22.0	0.997797	9990422	1.003262	0.0014145
22.5	0.997682	9989922	1.003376	0.0014638
23.0	0.997565	9989412	1.003492	0.0015140
23.5	0.997445	9988889	1.003611	0.0015656
24.0	0.997323	9988358	1.003733	0.0016180
24.5	0.997198	9987814	1.003857	0.0016717
25.0	0.998071	9987260	1.003982	0.0017260
25.5	0.996941	9986694	1.004111	0.0017819
26.0	0.996810	9986124	1.004242	0.0018383
26.5	0.996676	9985540	1.004375	0.0018960
27.0	0.996539	9984943	1.004512	0.0019550
27.5	0.996400	9984337	1.004649	0.0020145
28.0	0.996259	9983723	1.004790	0.0020752
28.5	0.996116	9983099	1.004933	0.0021369
29.0	0.995971	9982467	1.005077	0.0021995
29.5	0.995823	9981821	1.005225	0.0022633
30.0	0.995673	9981167	1.005375	0.0023280

procedure. It holds in general, that for calibration weighing should be absolute, i.e. with accurate weights, and not merely precise ones (p. 24), but as balances of lower sensitivity are usually used for calibrations, the accuracy being of the order of milligrams, sets of precise weights suffice provided the reference weight is not grossly in error.

A typical example, calibration of a 25-ml pipette at 20.5 °C, gave the following result (f = 1.002937)

Weight of beaker plus water, g	Weight of water, g	Volume of water, ml
42.179		
67.097	24.918	24.991
92.017	24.920	24.993
116.940	24.923	24.996
	mean	24.993

Correction: 24.993 − 25.000 = − 0.007 ml

We do not usually take into consideration buoyancy and changes of the vessel volume with temperature, if we are obtaining the true volume for one temperature only. When calibrating vessels, the volume data of which relate to a normal working temperature of 20° or 25 °C, we must make a correction for (a) the expansion of water with increase in temperature, (b) air buoyancy and (c) the expansion of glass with increase in temperature. In this case the calculation is rather lengthy, and it is simpler to use a compilation of data such as Table 2.3 from which we read directly the individual corrections or their sum for a litre of water of temperature t °C, weighed with brass weights in air of 50 % relative humidity and a pressure of 760 mmHg. The sum of corrections $a + b + c$ is sometime called the make-weight; the weight of water, $G_{H_2O} = 1\,000 - (a + b + c)$. If the temperature of the water and surrounding air differ, we apply a correction of 4 mg for every degree of the difference, adding this correction if the air is warmer than the water; when calibrating at a pressure differing from 760 mmHg, we introduce a correction of 1.4 mg for 1 000 ml water for every mmHg of the difference, subtracting it from G_{H_2O} for higher pressures, adding it for lower pressures. For example: water at 18 °C, contained in a 250-ml flask, weighs 249.42 g; the air temperature is 23 °C, barometric pressure 740 mmHg. The corrections are: $(760 - 740) \times 0.0014 + (23 - 18) \times$ $\times 0.004 = 0.028 + 0.020 = 0.048$ g; we find from Table 2.3: $G_{H_2O}^{18°} = 997.508 + 0.048 = = 997.556$ g for one litre; for 250 ml this is $997.556/4 = 249.39$ g: the value found was 249.42, which is greater by 0.03 g and therefore the vessel volume is 250.03 ml.

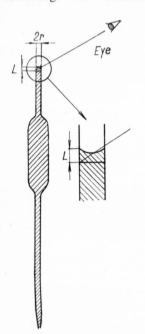

FIG. 2.1. Origin of the parallax and the error caused by the parallax in use of a pipette.

L — distance between the mark and the projection of the lower meniscus edge. The error of pipetting is thus given by the volume of a cylinder, of height L and base equal to the cross-section of the pipette in the vicinity of the mark.

2.7 Errors in measuring and making up solutions

In estimating the error of measuring solutions by means of a burette, we must consider on the one hand the error of setting the zero and reading the final volume (e.g. the error due to parallax), and on the other the error of the volume of the burette proper. When calibrated glassware is used, the possible volume error is known from the standards laid down and official calibration regulations. The magnitude of the error of reading the final volume may be estimated as half of the volume v given by the difference between two neighbouring marks, these being at least 1 mm apart. For burettes of 50-ml capacity and more, where the scale marks are about 1 mm or less apart, we must assume an error of reading equal to the smallest volume marked on the burette. In the titration proper, volume increments smaller

Table 2.3. Calibration of Volumetric Glassware

$t\ °C$	G_{H_2O}	Corrections			Makeweight $(a + b + c)$
		a	b	c	
15.0	997.924	0.874	1.077	0.125	2.076
15.5	997.864	0.950	1.074	0.112	2.136
16.0	997.798	1.030	1.072	0.100	2.202
16.5	997.729	1.113	1.070	0.088	2.271
17.0	997.658	1.199	1.068	0.075	2.342
17.5	997.585	1.287	1.066	0.062	2.415
18.0	997.508	1.378	1.064	0.050	2.492
18.5	997.427	1.472	1.063	0.038	2.573
19.0	997.346	1.568	1.061	0.025	2.654
19.5	997.261	1.668	1.059	0.012	2.739
20.0	997.173	1.770	1.057	0.000	2.827
20.5	997.083	1.874	1.055	—0.012	2.917
21.0	996.991	1.981	1.053	—0.025	3.009
21.5	996.896	2.091	1.051	—0.038	3.104
22.0	996.798	2.203	1.049	—0.050	3.202
22.5	996.697	2.318	1.047	—0.062	3.303
23.0	996.595	2.435	1.045	—0.075	3.405
23.5	996.490	2.555	1.043	—0.088	3.510
24.0	996.381	2.677	1.042	—0.100	3.619
24.5	996.270	2.802	1.040	—0.112	3.730
25.0	996.158	2.929	1.038	—0.125	3.842
25.5	996.043	3.059	1.036	—0.138	3.957
26.0	995.926	3.190	1.034	—0.150	4.074
26.5	995.806	3.324	1.032	—0.162	4.194
27.0	995.684	3.461	1.030	—0.175	4.316
27.5	995.560	3.600	1.028	—0.188	4.440
28.0	995.443	3.741	1.026	—0.200	4.567
28.5	995.304	3.884	1.024	—0.212	4.696
29.0	995.173	4.029	1.023	—0.225	4.827
29.5	995.040	4.177	1.021	—0.238	4.960
30.0	994.904	4.327	1.019	—0.250	5.069

Corrections are for *(a)* expansion of water, *(b)* buoyancy, *(c)* expansion of glass mean coefficient 2.5×10^{-5} ml/deg.

than one drop have to be taken for these estimates really to be fulfilled.

When a solution is measured with a graduated pipette, where the liquid stream is not stopped by closing a tap, practical tests have shown that the value of the absolute error is double that of burettes. For this reason it is preferable to measure from a burette volumes for which single-mark pipettes are not made (e.g. 4.8 ml), rather than from a graduated pipette.

When solutions are delivered from single-mark pipettes, or are made up to a given volume in volumetric flask, the error may be estimated as follows: with conventional methods of work, the error in adjusting the meniscus is usually not greater than 2 mm for the distance L in the case of large-volume wide-necked flasks, and 1 mm for single-mark pipettes and smaller flasks (250 ml or less).

The difference between the true and the assumed volume is then given by the volume of the cylinder $\pi r^2 L$ (Fig. 2.1), where r is given by the standard for the apparatus or can be measured. For medium volumes (e.g.

Table 2.4

Type of glassware	Volume, ml	Error of reading in ml	Permissible deviation in ml, according to official calibration instructions					Overall absolute error in ml when using glassware calibrated according to official instructions					Overall absolute error in ml according to Doerffel
			Czecho-slovakia	Ger-many	USA	GB A	GB B	Czecho-slovakia	Ger-many	USA	GB A	GB B	
Burettes	10	0.025	0.020	0.020	0.020	0.020	0.040	0.045	0.045	0.045	0.045	0.065	0.02
	25	0.050	0.030	0.030	0.030	0.030	0.050	0.080	0.080	0.080	0.080	0.100	0.03 (30 ml)
	50	0.100	0.040	0.040	0.050	0.050	0.100	0.140	0.140	0.150	0.150	0.200	0.04
One-mark pipettes	1	0.010	0.06	—	—	0.007	0.015	0.016	—	—	0.017	0.025	—
	2	0.020	0.06	0.006	0.006	0.010	0.020	0.026	0.026	0.026	0.030	0.040	—
	5	0.014	0.010	0.010	0.010	0.015	0.030	0.026	0.024	0.029	0.029	0.044	—
	10	0.019	0.015	0.015	0.020	0.020	0.040	0.034	0.034	0.039	0.039	0.059	—
	25	0.031	0.025	0.025	0.025	0.030	0.060	0.056	0.056	0.056	0.061	0.091	—
	50	0.037	0.035	0.035	0.050	0.040	0.080	0.072	0.072	0.087	0.077	0.117	—
Graduated pipettes	2	0.020	—	—	0.010	0.006	0.010	—	—	0.030	0.026	0.030	0.06
	5	0.015	—	—	0.020	0.010	0.020	—	—	0.035	0.025	0.035	—
	10	0.025	—	—	0.030	0.030	0.050	—	—	0.055	0.055	0.075	0.020
	30	0.060	—	—	0.050	—	—	—	—	0.110	—	—	0.025 (25 ml)
Volumetric flasks	25	0.050	0.015	0.020	0.030	0.03	0.06	0.065	0.095	0.080	0.080	0.110	—
	50	0.075	0.020	0.050	0.050	0.05	0.10	0.095	0.170	0.125	0.125	0.125	—
	100	0.120	0.050	0.080	0.080	0.08	0.15	0.170	0.260	0.200	0.200	0.270	0.08
	250	0.180	0.110	0.140	0.120	0.15	0.30	0.290	0.490	0.300	0.330	0.480	0.08
	500	0.350	0.140	0.180	0.150	0.25	0.50	0.490	0.680	0.500	0.600	0.850	0.14
	1 000	0.500	0.180	0.350	0.300	0.40	0.80	0.680	1.330	0.800	0.900	1.300	0.25
	2 000	1.000	0.350	—	0.500	0.60	1.20	1.330	—	1.500	1.600	2.200	0.50

100 ml) a precision of about $\pm 0.01\%$ may be expected if suitable equipment is used.

The values of absolute errors, determined from these considerations, are summarized in Table 2.4. The relative error is then easily determined from Eq. 1.5.

For example the absolute error of titration with a 25-ml burette (Table 2.4) is, $d = 0.08$ ml: with a consumption of 20.0 ml the relative error is $\varepsilon = \dfrac{0.08 \times 100}{20} = 0.4\%$.

With piston-type burettes, of course, the error caused by parallax need not be considered. The reproducibility of volumes measured by means of piston-type burettes is influenced mainly by circumstances such as the end play of the micrometer, or the lowest volume which can be separated from the burette ("drop error"), though the latter can be avoided by immersion of the burette tip in the solution titrated.

2.8 Sample weighing

In section 2.3 where we discussed the relative error of weighing, we stated that the relative error of weighing very small masses is too great. In practical work, however, we cannot always avoid using small samples, e.g. when analysing a sample consisting mainly of the component to be determined, or when determining the titre of a volumetric solution. The relative error of weighing may be decreased, to a certain extent, by weighing a larger amount of the sample, dissolving it, diluting to a given volume and taking aliquots by pipette. Use of aliquots is usually essential when we are carrying out a complete analysis from a single weighed sample, and very often minor components are determined on samples weighed individually, while the main components are determined on aliquots from a solution derived from a large sample.

To decide whether it is more suitable to weigh a sample directly or to prepare a stock solution and take aliquots, we must calculate the relative errors concerned. Thus, e.g. we are to weigh a sample of 50 mg: the relative error of weighing ($d = 0.2$ mg) is $\varepsilon_1 = \dfrac{2 \times 0.2 \times 100}{50} = 0.80\%$, but if a 0.5-g sample is weighed, dissolved and diluted to 250 ml, and aliquots of 25 ml are taken, the relative error of obtaining the 50-mg sample is scarcely half this: $\varepsilon_2 = \dfrac{2 \times 0.2 \times 100}{500} + \dfrac{0.330 \times 100}{250} + \dfrac{0.061 \times 100}{25} = 0.456\%$. (Values of absolute errors of diluting and pipetting are taken from Table 2.4.) On the other hand, there is no sense in preparing a stock solution for a 0.2-g sample, because $\varepsilon_1 = \dfrac{2 \times 0.2 \times 100}{200} = 0.20\%$, while with a sample of 2 g, dilution to 250 ml and aliquots of 25 ml, the maximum relative error is $\varepsilon_2 = \dfrac{2 \times 0.2 \times 100}{2\,000} + \dfrac{0.330 \times 100}{250} + \dfrac{0.061 \times 100}{25} = 0.4\%$. Though the error of weighing proper is decreased to a negligible value, the pipetting error alone (0.24%) is greater than the error of weighing in the first case.

The amount of stock solution and magnitude of the aliquot taken should be selected with due regard to the subsequent analytical procedure, but the choice is not very binding. For example the 0.05-g sample in the preceding case may be obtained not only by weighing 0.5 g, diluting to 250 ml and taking 25 ml, but also by weighing 62.5 mg into a 25 ml flask and pipetting 20 ml or by weighing 50 g, diluting to one litre and taking 1 ml. Again, choice is facilitated by calculation of the maximum relative error: in the first case, if a 30-ml one-mark pipette is used, we have $\varepsilon_1 =$

$$= \frac{2 \times 0.2 \times 100}{62.5} + \frac{0.080 \times 100}{25} + \frac{0.061 \times 100}{20} = 0.64\% + 0.32\% + 0.31\% = 1.27\%;$$

in the second case, $\varepsilon_2 = \dfrac{2 \times 0.5 \times 100}{50\,000} + \dfrac{1.600 \times 100}{1\,000} + \dfrac{0.016 \times 100}{1} = 0.02\% + 0.16\% +$

$+ 1.60\% = 1.78\%$.

In both cases the relative error is greater than the error of weighing a sample of 50 mg, and of course also greater than the error of making up to 250 ml and taking an aliquot of 25 ml.

To summarize: if too large an aliquot is taken, the sample used to make the parent solution will not be much bigger than one weighed direct, and the improvement in the relative error of weighing does not compensate for the errors of making up the solution and using the pipette: with too small an aliquot, the errors of weighing, and sometimes of making up the solution, become negligible, but the pipette itself is relatively imprecise. Aliquot samples are of practical significance when they permit the reduction of the sampling error to negligible proportions, and should consist of 1/10 to 1/2 of the stock solution, the volume chosen being from 10 to 50 ml [47, 55].

Much more accurate sampling can be achieved by making up the stock solution by weight, and weighing out portions of it for analysis. This procedure also has the advantage of precluding the experimenter from making parallel determinations agree with each other by making, unconsciously, appropriate errors in reading the burette.

2.9 Titre of the volumetric solution

The titre of a volumetric solution, i.e. the value x_3 from Eq. 1.10, is usually determined rather precisely, as already mentioned in section 1.6, so the relative error ε_{x_3} may often be neglected in comparison to the errors ε_{x_1} and ε_{x_2}; if the titre is incorrectly determined, a systematic error is introduced into all the results of the analyses.

Practically, the titre is determined by titration of a primary standard which is either weighed out direct or – a less reliable procedure – taken by pipette from a stock solution. The relative error of determining the titre is then equal to the sum of the relative errors of weighing and of the titration proper. The value of the titre therefore represents not only the deviation of the actual concentration of the volumetric solution from its nominal concentration, but also – a fact which is specially important when a burette with automatic "zero-setting" by means of an overflow device is used – the uncertainty of reading the burette, setting the zero, and locating the end-point. Corrections should be applied for the true volume of the burette used to determine the titre, and this burette should then be used for all titrations with the solution standardized.

The error calculated in the conventional manner must, in this case, be regarded as a "maximum" error, because the titre determination is usually repeated several times and the actual error may be made virtually negligible by the calculation of the mean, especially if the errors concerned are mainly random in character. DOERFFEL [47] mentions, in a very interesting paper, an example showing that the maximum relative error of preparation of a volumetric solution of exact concentration by dissolving a standard substance and making up to a given volume is usually lower − provided the work is done very carefully − than the error of determining the titre of a solution of approximate normality.

2.10　Physical measurements in practical analysis

In physical and physico-chemical methods the procedure is generally such that the concentration of the substance to be determined is measured in a previously prepared solution by means of measuring a quantity related to the concentration. The result is then given by Eq. 1.12 (p. 14)

$$p = \frac{1}{x_1} \cdot f(x_2)$$

It should, however, be kept in mind that the function $f(x_2)$ may be of such a character that x_1 and x_2 need not be linearly related, as we have assumed up to now. The exact solution of the relation between the error of the result and the errors ε_{x_1} and ε_{x_2} will not be simple in this case, although it may be simplified by the assumption (which is not always justified) that in a narrow range of values of x_1 and x_2 the dependence of x_2 on x_1 is approximately linear; in this case the relative error of the result is calculated as the sum of ε_{x_1}, ε_{x_2}, and possibly also ε_{x_3}. Even here, however, the conditions must be adjusted in such a way that the absolute value of the quantity measured should not be too small compared to the absolute error of measurement. In practice we sometimes succeed in adjusting the conditions in such a way that $f(x_2)$ is linear at least in a certain concentration range, even with those methods where linearity cannot be assumed in general. This is a great advantage in routine analyses.

Naturally it is not always easy to estimate the absolute error of physical measurement. We may measure a deviation directly on a scale (digital reading) or from a graph obtained on a recording instrument. Alternatively we may use a null-point method in which the signal measured is transduced and made part of a Wheatstone bridge or is compensated in some other way; a dial reading is then taken to find the degree of compensation required. Values on scales must be read in such a way as to avoid parallax errors: of great advantage are scales fitted with a mirror, or adjusted in such a way that the reference point, most often fitted with a vernier, is located beside the scale, not between it and the observer. Digital reading is very simple: it is either discontinuous and the last digit of the value of the quantity measured is estimated by eye, or the scale (if it is linear) is fitted with a vernier. Reading on a graph obtained with a recording instrument means measuring lengths or areas below curves. This problem is discussed in reference [10]. The magnitude of the absolute error of a reading, i.e. the extent to which the reading can be made reliably, can only be decided upon from experience. One way of doing it in the case of a null-point instrument is to find the change in reading caused by moving the indicator needle until it is just perceptibly out of register with the null-point; this should be done for both directions of movement. The relative error of the reading is given by the ratio

$$\varepsilon = \frac{100m}{M}$$

where m is the smallest reliably determined difference of values of the quantity measured and M is the absolute value of the quantity measured, read on the instrument.

In calculating the result of a physico-chemical analysis we generally use for x_2 in Eq. 1.9 or 1.12, the measured value M or a value calculated from it. The amount of a substance determined in a given volume, i.e. the concentration c_2, is sometimes directly proportional to M or is related to it by some simple function. This dependence is sometimes the consequence of a natural law (the Ilkovič law in polarography, Lambert-Beer law in spectrophotometry etc.). In practice we almost always determine this relationship graphically by means of a number of experiments, obtaining a calibration curve, which is then used to read c_2; this is essential if the relationship is non-linear.

Details of the construction and use of calibration curves are given in the monograph [10].

Consider a linear function $c = f(M)$, passing through the origin of the co-ordinate system. In this case we may use a single standard instead of a calibration curve; then

$$\frac{c_2}{c_1} = \frac{M_2}{M_1} \tag{2.5}$$

where c_2 is the concentration required, c_1 the concentration of the standard, M_2 and M_1 are the corresponding measured values.

This relationship is valid only if the function $M = f(c)$ is strictly linear. If this method is employed when linearity holds only for a certain concentration range, it is essential for c_1 to be approximately equal to c_2. The relative error of determining an unknown concentration by comparison with a standard is given by the simple relation

$$\varepsilon = \frac{m_{M_1} \cdot M_2 + m_{M_2} \cdot M_1}{M_1 \cdot M_2} \tag{2.6}$$

where m_M is the absolute error of the measurement. For the case of $c_1 = c_2 = c$, where we also may assume $m_{M_1} = m_{M_2}$ it holds that

$$\varepsilon = \frac{2m_M \cdot M}{M^2} = \frac{2m_M}{M} \tag{2.7}$$

It is generally more accurate to use a calibration curve than to use a single standard, because the slope of the line represents the mean value of f in Eq. 1.12, derived from several measurements.

Sometimes the standard is added to the solution analysed, and the measurement is repeated; this method, mainly employed in polarography and sometimes in spectrophotometric determinations, is called the *standard addition method*.

In practice we usually dilute an aliquot v_1 of the analysed solution (concentration c_1) to a certain volume V and measure, obtaining reading M_1; to another aliquot v_1 we add a volume v_0 of standard solution of concentration c_0 and again dilute to V, and obtain reading M_0. Then the concentration of the sample is given by $c_1 = c_0 v_0 M_1/v_1(M_0 - M_1)$. Sometimes the standard is added to a sample solution that has already been measured; if the volume added is v_0 as before, then the relationship is $c_1 = c_0 v_0 M_1/[M_0(v_0 + v_1) - M_1 v_1]$.

The *internal standard method* is frequently used in emission spectrography, in which case a known amount, the same in every case, of a certain element is added directly to the sample and evaluation is done by comparing the intensity of the line of the internal standard with that of the line of the element to be determined. Naturally we need a calibration graph, in which we plot the intensity ratio of the two lines measured, as a function of the amount of the element determined. The function need not be linear; indeed, the calibration graph generally has its points scattered and must be dealt with by special techniques (p. 138).

If with a linear relation $M = f(c)$ the calibration line does not pass through the origin, we can try a blank experiment and subtract its value from the measured values M. If the line now passes through the origin, comparison with a standard becomes possible, or the standard addition method may be used, the value of the blank being subtracted from M_1 as well as from M_2 before substitution in the equation. The problem of determining and reading the blank value becomes very significant if very small values of M are being measured, i.e. especially in the determination of trace elements. We shall come back to this problem later (p. 129).

In general, if a measurement is being carried out by means of comparison with a standard, the most correct procedure is one in which the concentration measured is approximately equal to that of the standard, and the standard and analysed samples are of approximately the same overall composition. When a calibration curve is used, it is again essential that the measured quantities should have values lying in the centre of the range for which the graph has been constructed. To amplify this section, the study by KIENITZ [72], and especially the newer study by EHRLICH and GERBATSCH [59] may be recommended.

As an example of optimization of physical measurements let us consider two measurements employed very frequently in analytical practice, i.e. absorbance, and height of polarographic waves. The mathematical solution to the problem, i.e. searching for the minimum error of the result as the function of errors of individual measurements, was indicated in section 1.5; since it is not a simple process, we shall only mention the practically applicable results.

Absorbance measurement, used in colorimetric and spectrophotometric determinations, is in principle the measurement of the ratio of the intensities of the incident light, I_0, and transmitted light, I_t:

$$A = \log \frac{I_0}{I_t} = k \cdot s \cdot c \qquad (2.8)$$

The absorbance A, according to the Lambert-Beer law, is linearly dependent on the concentration of the coloured (light-absorbing) substance.

In Eq. 2.8 k denotes the absorptivity, s the layer thickness, determined practically by the size of the cell employed, and c the concentration. Since k and s are constants for a given measurement, the error of the determination is given in principle by the error of the measurement of A.

It follows from a calculation [28, 38, 94] of the dependence of the error of absorbance measurement on the absorbance value in the case of absolute measurement, that the entire measurement is subject to the least relative error ($\varepsilon = 2\cdot7\%$) at $A = 0\cdot434$; the relative measurement error in the range $A = 0\cdot2$ to $0\cdot7$ is only slightly larger. Thus it is of advantage to select such a concentration in spectrophotometric measurements (or to select such a cell for a given concentration) as to bring the absorbance as far as possible into this range.

On measurement by the differential method, i.e. comparison with a standard of known concentration of the coloured substance, i.e. when measuring according to the relation

$$A_2 - A_1 = \log\frac{I_0}{I_2} - \log\frac{I_0}{I_1} = \log\frac{I_1}{I_2} = k \cdot s(c_2 - c_1) \qquad (2.9)$$

where quantities denoted by the subscripts 1 and 2 relate to the standard and sample respectively, FAUSS [61] has found, in full agreement with what has been said above, that for $A_1 > 0\cdot434$ the measurement is subject to minimum error when $A_2 = A_1$.

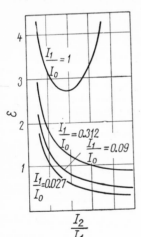

SVEHLA, PÁLL and ERDEY [94] have recently carried out a thorough study of the error of differential spectrophotometric determination, deriving a relation for the overall relative error where the dependence of the error on the absorbance value is given by the formula

$$\varepsilon = \frac{0\cdot4343}{\dfrac{I_2}{I_1}\left(\log\dfrac{I_2}{I_1} + \log\dfrac{I_1}{I_0}\right)} \qquad (2.10)$$

The graphical representation of the dependence of this function on the ratio I_2/I_1, i.e. the ratio of transmittances of the reference and the analysed solutions, indicates that the shape of the curve depends on the value of I_1/I_0, i.e. in principle on the transmittance of the reference solution. Figure 2.2 shows the course of the error-curve for different values of I_1/I_0. The curve for I_1/I_0 actually represents the case of direct spectro-

FIG. 2. 2. Connection of ε with ratio of absorbances of standard and sample.

photometric analysis ($I_1 = I_0$): the other curves, which in the region of $I_2/I_1 \leqq 1$ have no extreme, apply to different cases of differential spectrophotometry. Evidently, differential spectrophotometry is always subject to a lower error than is direct spectrophotometry.

In determining concentrations by measuring the height of the polarographic wave i_d there holds, according to the Ilkovič equation [68] a linear relation between i_d and c. The procedure usually involves the use of a calibration curve or the standard addition method. In the standard addition method, the solution analysed of an unknown concentration c_1 is first polarographed; we obtain a wave-height i_{d_1}. Now a certain volume v_0 of the standard solution, of a concentration c_0 is added to the original volume of the solution analysed, v_1, and another polarogram is recorded; the wave-height, i_{d_0}, is obtained. The concentration c_1 is calculated from the relation

$$c_1 = \frac{i_{d_1} \cdot c_0 \cdot v_0}{i_{d\hat{o}_1}(v_1 + v_0) - i_{d_1}v_1}$$ (2.11)

Opinions as to the most favourable conditions of application of the standard addition method in polarography differ: KOLTHOFF and LINGANE [19] think that the method gives the most accurate results if the standard addition is selected so that $i_{d_1} = 2i_{d_2}$. MEITES [79] believes that i_{d_1} should be substantially greater than i_{d_2}. REINMUTH [83] criticized the work done by Meites, and searched for the dependence of the error on the ratio i_{d_1}/i_{d_2}, taking into account the capacitive current i_0. Practically at the same time, SCHEJTANOV [88] set out from a criticism of the work of Meites; differing from Reinmuth, he considered the influence of the volume change when the standard is added, establishing the values of volume changes and wave-height ratios for which the error of the determination is minimum. However, Schejtanov did not consider the error caused by lack of precision in making the standard addition. ECKSCHLAGER [51] has shown that the discrepancies in the views of these authors are caused by the fact that they have simplified their considerations in different ways. He found a solution by introducing a function H, given by

$$H = \frac{100(1 + \beta) < p(1 < \beta)}{p\{100(1 + \beta) - p\}} \times 100$$ (2.12)

where $p = 100i_{d_1}/i_{d_2}$ and $\beta = v_0/v_2$, v_0 being the volume of the standard addition and v_2 the initial volume. He has tabulated the value of the function H, representing that component of the maximum relative error that can be influenced by the experimental conditions, for different values of the ratio of wave-heights p and for different volume changes β, finding that the error achieved a minimum at different values of p for different values of β. It follows from this work that determinations by means of the standard addition method are most precise when rather a large volume is used for the standard addition and when i_{d_2} is from $0.6i_{d_1}$ to $0.8i_{d_1}$. It should be noted however, that neither the ratio of wave-heights nor the volume change caused by the standard addition has such a large influence on the final error of the determination as does the error of measuring out the solution volumes, which has not been taken into account at all in the earlier studies. Another very important requirement is that of the greatest possible sensitivity, i.e. that i_{d_1} should represent full-scale deflection on the recording instrument.

Compared to the standard addition method, the use of a calibration curve has the great advantage that it allows precise determinations in a relatively wide concentration range of 10^{-3} to 10^{-5}M.

2.11 Indirect two-component analysis

The determination of two substances A and B in a mixture may, in some cases, be carried out indirectly without separation of the two components, e.g. by weighing the mixture, converting the two components into other compounds and weighing again, or by determining the sum of the two components and then determining one of them, or by measuring the absorbance of the solution at various wavelengths, etc. It holds in all cases, that

$$M_1 = k_{A,1}c_A + k_{B,1}c_B \qquad (2.13)$$

$$M_2 = k_{A,2}c_A + k_{B,2}c_B \qquad (2.14)$$

where M_1, M_2 are the results of measurement under different conditions (sums of the weight of the two components in the form of different compounds, absorbances at different wavelengths etc.), $k_{A,1}$, etc., are the respective stoichiometric factors, extinction coefficients etc., c_A and c_B are the amounts of the substances A and B. The result of an indirect two-component analysis is evaluated by solving two equations of two variables e.g. by means of determinants or of a nomogram. Determinant calculations and the construction of the nomogram are explained in the monograph on graphic methods [10].

Let us now investigate the errors of two-component analysis. Denoting the absolute error of measuring the quantity M by the symbol d_M, and assuming that $d_{M_1} = d_{M_2} = d_M$ (remembering that this is rather an oversimplification), we find for the relative error of the result

$$\varepsilon_A = \frac{d_M}{M_A} = \frac{k_{B,1} + k_{B,2} \cdot d_M}{k_{B,2}M_1 - k_{B,1}M_2} \qquad (2.15)$$

and quite in analogy to this

$$\varepsilon_B = \frac{d_M}{M_B} = \frac{k_{A,1} + k_{A,2} \cdot d_M}{k_{A,1}M_2 - k_{A,2}M_1} \qquad (2.16)$$

It is evident that not only the value of the absolute measurement error but also the magnitude or the ratio of the values of the measured quantities M_1 and M_2 and of the factors k will influence the relative error ε. In two-component analysis it is difficult to select optimum conditions, because the overall error of the determination is mainly dependent on the composition of the analysed mixture, being generally larger than with direct determinations.

Under certain conditions, multi-component analysis is also possible, e.g. by means of measuring absorbance at various wavelengths. When a mixture of n components is being analysed, by measuring extinction values at n wavelengths, the calculation of the result involves the solution of n ebuations with n variables. The results may, of course, be subject to a certain error, especially if one of the measurements is subject to rather a large error. More reliable results may be obtained by measuring the extinction at $m > n$ wavelengths and homogenizing the results by the least squares method. The numerical solution of such a problem is difficult and lengthy unless data-processing equipment is available. BARNETT and BARTOLI [40] have used a computer to calculate the results fo multi-component spectrophotometric analysis for $m > n$ with evaluation by the least-squares method, including a correction for deviations from the Lambert-Beer law. DOERFFEL has studied the problem of precision in indirect multi-component analyses [8], arriving — with full justification — at rather a sceptical view. He mainly stresses the need of exact work in multi-component analysis and the necessity of knowing the exact values of the individual coefficients.

2.12 Checking the accuracy of instruments: calibration and setting

A possible source of systematic error of physico-chemical analytical methods is constituted by the various errors and imperfections of instruments and apparatus, which may lead to inaccurate or badly reproducible results of measurement. Frequently even a slight disagreement of the beginning of the scale with the position of the indicator with the instrument switched off, decreased sensitivity of the instrument in a certain range of measured values, slow reaction of the recording instrument or increased "noise" etc., suffice to cause such inaccuracy. Another source of systematic error of a series of measurements may be that the relation between the measured value M and the concentration of the component determined (see sections 1.6 and 2.10) may vary to some extent under different external influences when measured by a given instrument. All these, as well as other circumstances which are difficult to foresee, can often only be determined by comp ison of the values obtained with the true values of standards. Such checking of instruments is an essential part of their use.

Thus the analyst is forced to calibrate instruments, i.e. to elucidate the analytical significance of individual data read on the instrument when a standard of known composition is being measured. Of course the standard must be perfectly pure and must have a precisely defined composition, otherwise calibration will cause systematic errors. In every thorough calibration carried out by means of a large series of measurements, we study not only the absolute values obtained, but also the validity of the relationship involved, especially whether there is a departure from linearity when linearity is expected according to theory. If perfect linearity and good reproducibility of repeated measurements is proved, the entire calibration may sometimes be replaced by simple setting, i.e. adjustment of the zero value and comparison of one or two measured values with the theoretical values calculated for the standard, followed by adjustment of the scale or computation of a correction. If the instrument is being set for a given standard, it is of advantage for this standard to approach as far as possible the composition of the sample to be analysed.

Chapter 3

SPECIFIC ERRORS
OF INDIVIDUAL METHODS

3.1 Introduction

The errors so far discussed have occurred in the measurement of physical properties of substances, i.e. in the quantitative expression of these properties in certain units. These properties, the magnitude of which is in a certain, precisely definable, relation to the amount and nature of the component to be determined and makes it possible to carry out measurements for analytical purposes, are called the analytical properties of substances.

In the course of an analysis, however, we have to carry out not only the final measurement, but also in most cases a preliminary analytical procedure, which may itself be a source of errors greater than those occurring in the measurement proper. Analytical procedures are generally based on the chemical properties of substances, e.g. the formation of compounds permitting an immediate measurement or separation, though physical properties are also used to achieve separations, e.g. solubility, volatility, migration in an electrical field, etc. The properties utilized for analytical procedures are not always ideal: they are subject to a number of drawbacks which affect the precision and accuracy of the analytical results by causing specific errors in a given method. For example, "insoluble" precipitates are always soluble to a certain extent, no extraction process can be regarded as perfect, and so on.

Within the scope of this chapter it is impossible to discuss all the possible causes which might lead to error in individual analytical processes. Moreover, every analytical method, and every one of its modifications, is subject to its own specific errors. In what follows we shall mention only the very general sources of error, particularly those in which the magnitude of the error can be expressed numerically. More details will be found in the original literature [15, 20, 22, 27, 30].

3.2 The Guldberg-Waage law

The course of a procedure used for a chemical analysis may often be derived from physico-chemical laws. We then use the mathematical formulae which express these laws quantitatively, to calculate the error which may occur in the procedure.

One of the main demands is that the analytical procedure should be as perfectly quantitative as possible. Since we are dealing in most cases with reversible reactions, we make use of the Guldberg-Waage law, which informs us of the degree to which a certain reaction will proceed. In the reaction

$$A + nB = AB_n,$$

the equilibrium is defined by

$$K = \frac{[AB_n]}{[A][B]^n} \tag{3.1}$$

where K is the concentration equilibrium constant of the reaction and $[A]$, $[B]$ and $[AB_n]$ are the molar concentrations of the substances A, B and AB_n in the reaction mixture after establishment of the equilibrium. The reason for using the concentrations instead of the activities of the species is that it makes the calculations simpler, and is completely satisfactory for most purposes. Moreover, the activity coefficients are seldom all known accurately, and since possible deviations would become apparent only at ionic strengths greater than 0.1, we can assume that in reasonably dilute solutions there is no great error introduced by this simplification.

Let us now assume that substance A is converted quantitatively into the reaction product AB_n by the addition of substance B. If the reaction were to proceed rapidly and quantitatively, it would be enough to mix together the two reaction components in the correct stoichiometric ratio of their concentrations, namely c_A for A and $c_B = n \cdot c_A$ for B, and the concentration of the final product would be $c_{AB_n} = c_A$, the reaction mixture then containing no free initial substances, i.e. neither A nor B. Since, however, the reaction is invariably not completely quantitative, and an equilibrium is set up, the concentration of the free A present will be given by

$$[A] = \frac{[AB_n]}{K[B]^n} \tag{3.2}$$

If we denote by c_A the total molar concentration of substance A, irrespective of the species containing it, we obtain $c_A = [AB_n] + [A]$. The quantity c_A is often called the analytical concentration of A. If the reaction is substantially complete (equilibrium shifted to the right) then $[A]$ may be neglected in comparison to c_A, and so

$$[A] = \frac{c_A}{[B]^n} \cdot \frac{1}{K} \tag{3.3}$$

From this it is seen that the concentration of A that has not reacted depends on the equilibrium constant K as well as on c_A and $[B]$. It further follows from Eq. 3.3, that if we wish to decrease the value of $[A]$, we must increase $[B]$, i.e. work with an excess of substance B.

Thus, if we try to convert 10 ml of 0.1 M silver solution "quantitatively" into the diamminesilver(I) complex $[Ag(NH_3)_2]^+$, for which $K = 1.47 \times 10^7 \; l^2 \cdot mole^{-2}$, by the addition of such an amount of ammonia that after dilution of the mixture to 100 ml an ammonia concentration of 10^{-3} mole . l^{-1} would still be present, then the concentration of the free silver ions would be, to a first approximation

$$Ag^+ = \frac{[Ag(NH_3)_2^+]}{K[NH_3]^2} = \frac{(10^{-2} \text{ mole . } l^{-1})}{(1.47 \times 10^7 \; l^2 . mole^{-2})(10^{-3} \text{ mole.} l^{-1})^2} =$$

$$= 6 \cdot 8 \times 10^{-4} \text{ mole . } l^{-1} \tag{3.4}$$

This value of $[Ag^+]$ then represents the absolute error in the conversion of the silver ion into the complex ion $[Ag(NH_3)_2]^+$: the relative error $\varepsilon = \dfrac{6.8 \times 10^{-4} \times 100}{10^{-2}} = 6.8\%$. This means that the reaction is only 93.2% complete. It is evident from Eq. 3.3 that complete conversion of A into AB_n is theoretically possible only by means of an infinitely large excess of component B. In practice we have to be satisfied with a reaction which is quantitative to such an extent that the relative error caused by incompleteness of the reaction can be neglected in comparison with the other errors.

Therefore, in the case of conversion of univalent silver ions into the diammine complex the question must be formulated in a different way: how large should the excess of ammonia be in the final mixture in order that the error caused by the incomplete character of the reaction would not be greater than some arbitrary value, e.g. 0.034%? First of all we must determine the corresponding error:

$$\varepsilon = \frac{[Ag^+]}{c_A} \cdot 100 = 0.034\% : c_A = 10^{-2}\ \text{mole} \cdot 1^{-1}$$

$$[Ag^+] = 3.4 \times 10^{-6}\ \text{mole} \cdot 1^{-1}$$

Since $[A] = c_A/K[B]$, $[B] = (c_A/K[A])$, we then obtain for the ammonia concentration

$$[NH_2] = \left\{ \frac{(10^{-2}\ \text{mole} \cdot 1^{-1})}{(1.47 \times 10^7\ 1^2 \cdot \text{mole}^{-2})(3.4 \times 10^{-6}\ \text{mole} \cdot 1^{-1})} \right\}^{\frac{1}{2}}$$

$$= 1.4 \times 10^{-2}\ \text{mole} \cdot 1^{-1} \tag{3.5}$$

This means that such an amount of ammonia must be added that the final concentration of its excess is 0.014 M, i.e. 34 ml of 0.1 M ammonia is needed.

Although in practice calculations of this type are seldom used in error calculations, it is essential to know and to be able to demonstrate that the quantitative character of an analytical equilibrium depends on the value of the equilibrium constant K and on the magnitude of the excess of the other reactants, and to realize that a reaction can never be completely quantitative, but that instead we always have to be satisfied with such a degree of "quantitativeness" that the error caused by the incompleteness of the reaction either does not endanger the desired accuracy of the final result or is less than the smallest error that can be detected in the measurements.

3.3 Errors in neutralization titrations

The basic reaction of neutralization titrations in aqueous medium is the reaction of hydrogen and hydroxyl ions: $H^+ + OH^- \rightleftharpoons H_2O$. In a solution of an acid, the hydrogen ion concentration $[H^+]$ is given by the extent of dissociation of the acid $HA \rightleftharpoons H^+ + A^-$, and the equilibrium established in the process is defined by

$$K = \frac{[H^+][A^-]}{[HA]} \tag{3.6}$$

where K is the dissociation constant. Some dissociation constants of acids are given in Table 3.1. In the course of the titration, i.e. during the process in which hydrogen and hydroxyl ions combine to form non-dissociated water molecules, the ratio of $[H^+]$ to $[OH^-]$ changes, but in such a way that the product $[H^+][OH^-] = 10^{-14}$ remains constant. At the equivalence point, when the stoicheiometric amount of hydroxyl ions has been added, no other acid is contained in the mixture except that which may be present owing to hydrolysis of the salt formed. The pH value at the equivalence point, the so-called titration exponent pT, is given by the relation pT = $= 7 + \frac{1}{2}$pK + log [A]. According to Tomíček [32] the pT value may be approximately estimated from the pK value of the acid as pT = pK + 2, provided that pT is less than 10. If the titration were continued until the pH was equal to pT, the result obtained ought to be absolutely correct except, of course, for other titration errors, such as errors in the burette calibration, reading errors, standardization of titrant, etc. In practice, however, the

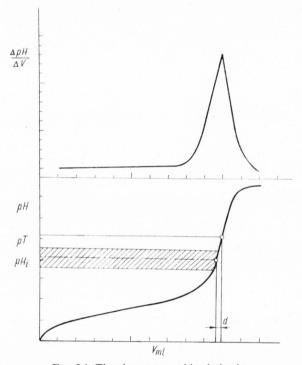

FIG. 3.1. Titration curve and its derivative.

titration is carried out in the presence of an indicator, of which the colour change, indicating the end of the titration, need not occur precisely at the pH of the equivalence point, but may occur instead at a different pH value, denoted by pH$_i$. The error thus caused is called the titration or indicator error.

The source of the titration error may be illustrated by means of a titration curve showing the consumption of the volumetric solution required to achieve the pT and pH$_i$ values, Fig. 3.1. It is assumed for the discussion of the indicator error that an indicator has been used which is suitable for the titration. An error caused by the use of a distinctly unsuitable indicator belongs to the group of gross errors.

It remains to discuss the problem of the pH value at which the colour change of the indicator starts. An acid-base indicator is either a weak

Table 3.1. Dissociation Constants of Acids and Bases

Acid or Base	Formula	K_1	K_2	K_3
Boric acid	H_3BO_3	6.4×10^{-10}		
Phosphoric acid	H_3PO_4	1.1×10^{-2}	1.9×10^{-7}	3.6×10^{-13}
Carbonic acid	H_2CO_3	3.0×10^{-7}	6.0×10^{-11}	
Formic acid	$HCOOH$	2.0×10^{-4}		
Acetic acid	CH_3COOH	2.0×10^{-5}		
Oxalic acid	$(COOH)_2$	3.8×10^{-2}	3.5×10^{-5}	
Citric acid	$C_6H_8O_7$	8.0×10^{-4}	5.0×10^{-5}	2.0×10^{-6}
Tartaric acid	$C_2H_2(OH)_2 . (COOH)_2$	9.7×10^{-4}	9.0×10^{-5}	
Benzoic acid	C_6H_5COOH	6.8×10^{-5}		
Salicylic acid	$C_6H_4OHCOOH$	1.1×10^{-3}		
Ammonia	NH_4OH	1.8×10^{-5}		
Hydrazine	$(NH_2)_2$	2.0×10^{-6}		
Methylamine	CH_3NH_2	4.0×10^{-4}		
Dimethylamine	$(CH_3)_2NH$	5.5×10^{-4}		
Trimethylamine	$(CH_3)_3N$	6.5×10^{-5}		
α-Naphthylamine	$C_{10}H_7NH_2$	9.9×10^{-11}		
β-Naphthylamine	$C_{10}H_7NH_2$	2.0×10^{-9}		
Caffeine	$C_8H_{10}N_4O_2 . H_2O$	4.1×10^{-14}		
Theobromine	$C_7H_8N_4O_2$	4.8×10^{-14}		
Quinine	$C_{20}H_{24}N_2O_2 . 3 H_2O$	1.0×10^{-6}	1.3×10^{-10}	

acid or a weak base, and its undissociated form is of a different colour from the dissociated form. In other words, it is a substance which changes colour in accordance with the equilibria $HI \rightleftharpoons H^+ I^-$ or $IOH \rightleftharpoons I^+ + OH^-$, determined by the equilibrium constants

$$K_{HI} = \frac{[H^+][I^-]}{[HI]} \quad \text{or} \quad K_{IOH} = \frac{[I^+][OH^-]}{[IOH]} \tag{3.7}$$

The pH value decisive for the occurrence of a titration error is that at which a distinct colour change of the indicator sets in, i.e. the pH_i value. It is known from practice that such a colour change can only be registered visually over the range $10-90\,\%$ conversion of one form of the indicator into the other. If we define the concentration ratio of the two forms as

$$R = \frac{[HI]}{[I^-]} \quad \text{or} \quad \frac{[IOH]}{[I^+]} \tag{3.8}$$

then the pH_i value, i.e. the value at which a visible colour change of e.g. an acid indicator sets in, is given by

$$[H^+] = K_{HI} \cdot \frac{[HI]}{[I^-]} = K_{HI} \cdot R \tag{3.9}$$

The colour change starts at a hydrogen ion concentration $[H^+]_a = K_{HI} \cdot \frac{90}{10}$ i.e. at $pH_i = pH_{HI} - 0.95$, and ends at $[H^+]_e = K_{HI} \cdot \frac{10}{90}$ i.e. at $pH_i = pK_{HI} + 0.95$. A similar calculation may be used for alkaline indicators. Thus the calculations show that the pH range in which a colour change of the indicator takes place is $pH_i = pK_{HI} \pm 1$ for acid indicators and $pH_i = 14 - pH_{IOH} \pm 1$ for basic indicators.

The good agreement of these calculated values with the values determined experimentally for the colour change of the acid-base indicators most frequently used is shown in Table 3.2.

Table 3.2. Some Acid-Base Indicators

Indicator	Chemical Nature of Indicator	pK_{HI} pK_{IOH}	Region of Colour Change	
			pH_i	pOH_i
Methyl orange	Base	10.30		9.6 ... 11.1
Bromphenol blue	Acid	4.00	3.0 ... 4.6	
Methyl red	Acid	4.98	4.2 ... 6.2	
Neutral red	Base	7.15		6.0 ... 7.6
Bromthymol blue	Acid	7.08	6.0 ... 7.6	
Phenol red	Acid	7.85	6.4 ... 8.0	
Phenolphthalein	Acid	9.73	8.0 ... 10.2	

On the other hand, the pH_i value of an indicator may be used as a measure of its sensitivity to hydrogen ions. The higher the pH range in which the indicator changes colour, the smaller are the hydrogen ion concentrations which it can detect, i.e. the more sensitive it is to hydrogen ions.

It is also interesting to compare the sensitivity of indicators to hydrogen ions, as a function of the strength of the indicators as acids or bases. It is evident that indicators which are themselves weak acids (i.e. having higher pH_{HI} values) are more sensitive to acids than are strongly acidic indicators; e.g. methyl red ($pK_{HI} = 4.98$) changes colour at $[H^+] = 10^{-5}$ M, whereas phenolphthalein ($pK_{HI} = 9.73$, i.e. a far weaker acid), changes colour only at a value of $[H^+] = 10^{-9}$ M. Similarly, strongly basic indicators are more sensitive to acids than indicators of weaker basicity. Of course indicators sensitive to acids are less sensitive to bases, and vice versa. Details of the sensitivity and other interesting properties of indicators will be found in the monograph by TOMÍČEK [32].

Let us now demonstrate the calculation of the titration error e.g. in the titration of 25 ml of 0.1 M acetic acid ($K = 2 \times 10^{-5}$ mole . 1^{-1}) with 0.1 M sodium hydroxide. The precise end-point of the titration is calculated as follows: $pT = 7 + \frac{1}{2}pK + \frac{1}{2}\log [CH_3COO^-]$: $pK = -\log K = 4.7$, and $[CH_3COO^-]$ at the end of the titration is 5×10^{-2} mole . 1^{-1}, i.e. $pT = 8.7$. Thus the titration should be continued until this pH is reached. If phenolphthalein is used as indicator and the solution is titrated to the first observable pink colour, i.e. to pH_i of about 8, the titration error may be calculated.

In titration of a weak acid with a strong base, the equilibria

$$HA \rightleftharpoons H^+ + A^- \qquad K = \frac{[H][A]}{[HA]} \qquad (3.10)$$

$$H_2O \rightleftharpoons H^+ + OH^- \qquad K_w = [H][OH] \tag{3.11}$$

must be satisfied simultaneously.

Hence

$$\frac{[HA]K}{[A]} = \frac{K_w}{[OH]} \tag{3.12}$$

or

$$[OH] = \frac{K_w[A]}{K[HA]} \tag{3.13}$$

and since we have, in effect, for the hydrolysis of the salt,

$$A^- + H_2O \rightleftharpoons HA + OH^- \tag{3.14}$$

then

$$[OH] = [HA] \quad \text{and} \quad [A] = C_{HA} - [OH],$$

where C_{HA} is the analytical concentration of HA.

Then at the equivalence point

$$[HA] = \left\{ \frac{K_w}{K} \cdot (C_{HA} - [HA]) \right\}^{\frac{1}{2}}$$

or if

$$C_{HA} \gg [HA], \qquad \text{then} \qquad [HA] = \left(\frac{K_w}{K} \cdot C_{HA} \right)^{\frac{1}{2}} = [OH].$$

Hence the pH of the equivalence point is given by

$$pH = \frac{1}{2} pK - \frac{1}{2} \log K_w - \frac{1}{2} \log C_{HA} \tag{3.15}$$

$$pH = 7.0 + \frac{1}{2} pK - \frac{1}{2} \log C_{HA} \tag{3.16}$$

If the end-point fails to coincide with the equivalence point and occurs at some other pH, then the titration error is simply

$$\frac{\left\{ \frac{K_w}{[H]} - \left(\frac{K_w C_{HA}}{K} \right)^{\frac{1}{2}} \right\} \times 100\%}{C_{HA}} \tag{3.17}$$

The titration error can also be determined experimentally by recording the course of the titration potentiometrically and comparing the colour change of the indicator with the potential change, as illustrated in Fig. 3.1 (p. 45).

Let us now discuss the amount of indicator which is to be added to the titration mixture. In the case of one-colour indicators (e.g. phenolphthalein) the first observable colour is given by a certain minimum concentration of the coloured form of the indicator $[I^-]_{min}$. The hydrogen ion concentration at which this $[I^-]_{min}$ is achieved, is

$$[H^+] = \frac{K_{HI} \cdot c_i}{[I^-]_{min}} \tag{3.18}$$

K_{HI} and $[I^-]_{min}$ being constants and c_i the indicator concentration in the solution. This means that for a larger concentration c_i the minimum concentration of the coloured indicator form $[I^-]_{min}$ is achieved only with a larger hydrogen ion concentration, i.e. at a lower pH value, so the sensitivity of the indicator to bases increases. In the case of a two-colour indicator (e.g. methyl red) the effect of indicator concentration is not as distinct, because the resulting colour is determined by the concentration ratio of the two coloured forms, and not as in the first case by the concentration of one component. Moreover the situation is complicated by the fact that the human eye is frequently not equally sensitive for the two colour tones. As the indicators themselves are acids or bases, we must always keep in mind when using them, that only the essential minimum amount of the indicator should be present in the solution, not more than is necessary for the colour change to be distinguished.

3.4 The titration error of complexometric titrations

In recent years numerous authors have discussed the error occurring in complexometric titrations. KÖRBL and PŘIBIL [73] have generalized complexometric titrations to include acid-base titrations, and so has RINGBOM [26]. The error of complexometric titration depends, like all other titration errors, on the process used to detect the end-point. In principle two procedures are used: either the first excess of the titrant is indicated or the decrease of the concentration of a certain component below a given limit is detected. In the first case the titration error is calculated in the same way as in the case of precipitation titrations which are to be discussed in the next section. In the second case substances are used which form a complex compound of marked colour with the metal to be determined. This colour disappears or changes when the metal has been combined into a more stable complex, e.g. with EDTA. The substances used as indicators may be classified in two groups: the first includes those substances which are colourless in themselves, so that at the end of the titration the solution is decolorized, the second and far more important group is formed by organic dyes which have the properties of acid-base indicators and contain chelate-forming groups. KÖRBL, who has studied these dyes in detail, has called them metallochromic indicators. In a titration with a metallochromic indicator the end-point is marked by a change from the colour of the metal-indicator complex to the colour of the free indicator.

Let us now investigate the factors determining the titration error in complexometric titrations. In this case the absolute error is equal to the amount of metal which is not bound in a complex at the apparent equivalence point. The amount of metal converted into the complex is therefore mainly dependent on the sensitivity of the indicator used. This sensitivity depends on the one hand on the stability constant (or formation constant) of the complex, K, which is defined for the reaction of the metal with the indicator $M + I \rightleftharpoons MI$ by $K_I = [MI]/[M][I]$; on the other hand it depends on the indicator concentration, since the indicator itself also acts as complexing agent and competes with the titrant. As metallochromic indicators as well as complex-forming titrants are Lewis bases, it is understandable that the pH also influences the titration error of complexometric titrations.

When a two-colour metallochromic indicator is used, the colour of the solution is characterized by the ratio $A = [MI]/[I]$; as in the case of acid-base indicators the colour change takes place over the range from $A = 9$ to $A = 1/9$.

In the case of one-colour indicators the titration end-point is indicated when the concentration of the metal-indicator complex $[MI]$ has decreased to the limiting value $B = [MI]_{min}$, which is no longer observable. The value of $[MI]_{min}$ differs, of course, according to the molar absorptivity of the coloured complex.

First of all let us determine the optimum concentration of the metallochromic indicator by means of the relation which describes the dependence of the sensitivity of the indicator (U) on its concentration, using the equation

$$U = A \left(\frac{1}{K_I} + \frac{c_I}{A + 1} \right) \tag{3.19}$$

where c_I is the overall concentration of the indicator. Of course the reaction of the indicator is the more sensitive, the greater the change of the value of A caused by a small change of the metal concentration (free or bound to the indicator) or the closer the derivative $\dfrac{dU}{dA} = \dfrac{1}{K_I} + \dfrac{c_I}{(A + 1)^2}$ is to its minimum. The minimum occurs when $c_I = 0$, in agreement with the practical experience that it is best to add the smallest possible amount of metallochromic indicator. It also follows from the equation for the sensitivity that the indicator concentration is practically without influence when $c_I \leqq U$.

In the case of one-colour indicators, $U = B \left(\dfrac{1}{K_I . c_I} + 1 \right)$ and the first derivative $\dfrac{dU}{dB} = \dfrac{1}{K_I . c_I} + 1$ reaches a minimum when c_I is as large as possible. Here, a large amount of indicator must be added in order to eliminate as far as possible the dissociation of the coloured complex formed by the metal and indicator and in order that the smallest possible amount of metal should escape titration. For the calculation proper of the titration error it is essential to determine the actual sensitivity of the indicator under the given titration conditions. This sensitivity can either be determined experimentally or, if the values of K_I and c_I are known, it can be calculated from the relationships given above, for the range of A from $1/9$ to 9 or with a value of B determined experimentally. The relative error is obtained [62] from the formula $\varepsilon = (p - 1) \times 100\%$, where p, defined as the ratio of the metal concentration c_M and amount of titrant consumed, c_Y, may be determined from the relation $p = 1 - \dfrac{U}{c_M} + \dfrac{\alpha_Y}{U . K}$. In this equation $c_M = [M] + [MY]$ denotes the total concentration of the metal, and K is the stability constant of the complex formed by the metal and titrant; $K = [MY]/[M] [Y]$. The ratio K/α_Y represents the stability constant for a given pH value, the quantity α_Y, called by Ringbom the side-reaction coefficient, modifying the thermodynamic stability constant to take account of the degree of formation of the given complex at a given pH value.

Table 3.3 lists the $\log \alpha_Y$ values for various pH values for ethylenediamine-tetra-acetic acid. Table 3.4 gives the $\log K$ values needed for the calculation of the error in EDTA titrations.

Table 3.3. Values of $\log \alpha_y$ for EDTA

pH	$\log \alpha_Y$	pH	$\log \alpha_Y$	pH	$\log \alpha_Y$
0.0	21.18	3.0	10.63	6.0	4.65
0.2	20.39	3.2	10.16	6.2	4.34
0.4	19.59	3.4	9.71	6.4	4.06
0.6	18.42	3.6	9.28	6.6	3.79
0.8	18.01	3.8	8.86	6.8	3.55
1.0	17.20	4.0	8.45	7.0	3.32
1.2	16.45	4.2	8.04	7.5	2.78
1.4	15.68	4.4	7.65	8.0	2.26
1.6	14.93	4.6	7.23	8.5	1.77
1.8	14.21	4.8	6.84	9.0	1.29
2.0	13.52	5.0	6.45	9.5	0.83
2.2	12.79	5.2	6.06	10.0	0.45
2.4	12.24	5.4	5.69	11.0	0.07
2.6	11.67	5.6	5.05	12.0	0.00
2.8	11.13	5.8	4.98	14.0	0.00

Table 3.4. Stability Constants of Chelates of some Cations with EDTA ($pK_1 = 2.0$; $pK_2 = 2.76$; $pK_3 = 6.16$; $pK_4 = 10.26$)

Cation	$\log K_{MeY}$	Cation	$\log K_{MeY}$
Mg^{2+}	8.69	Co^{3+}	16.31
Ca^{2+}	10.96	Ni^{2+}	18.62
Sr^{2+}	8.63	Cu^{2+}	18.80
Ba^{2+}	7.76	Zn^{2+}	16.50
Mn^{2+}	14.04	Cd^{2+}	16.46
Fe^{2+}	14.33	Pb^{2+}	18.04
Fe^{3+}	25.1	Al^{3+}	16.13

The relative error is determined very easily by means of a nomogram published in the original paper by KÖRBL and PŘIBIL [73]. In this nomogram, values of U/c_M and $\alpha_Y/U \cdot K$ are read directly in per cent, their difference giving the total relative error. The nomogram is especially suitable for those cases where we can be satisfied with an approximate value for the relative error, and also of course in searching for the optimum conditions for a titration.

Let us now demonstrate the calculation of the relative error by means of an example: 20 ml of 0.01 M magnesium solution are titrated with 0.01 M EDTA at pH 9.5, Eriochrome Black T being used as indicator. From experience we know that $U = 5 \times 10^{-6}$ and from Tables 3.3 and 3.4 we obtain for magnesium the values of $\log K$ (8.69) and $\log \alpha_Y$ (0.83) at pH 9.5. At the titration end-point we find $c_M =$

$$= \frac{0.01 \times 20}{40} = 0.005M. \quad \text{Therefore} \quad p = 1 - \frac{U}{c_M} + \frac{\alpha_H}{U \cdot H} = 1.002: \quad \varepsilon = (p - 1) \times$$

$\times 100\% = 0.2\%$.

The same estimate of error would be obtained by using the nomogram. For details the reader should read the original paper [73].

The problem of sharpness of the colour change of the indicator at the equivalence point of a complexometric titration, which is very important for the accuracy of the result, has been studied by REILLEY and SCHMID [82, 90] and several others [26, 31, 66, 84].

3.5 Solubility of precipitates; titration error of precipitation titrations

A specific source of error in gravimetric analysis and precipitation titrations is the solubility of the precipitate. The equilibrium $AB_n =$ $= A + nB$, which is established on dissolution of a sparingly soluble substance AB_n, is characterized by the solubility product

$$K_{sp} = [A] [B]^n \qquad (3.20)$$

The concentrations [A] and [B] used in the solubility product must always be expressed as molarities. The K_{sp} values of some important substances are given in Table 3.5.

The calculation of the relative error caused by the dissolution of part of the precipitate in the course of washing by decantation is best clarified by means of an example: 0.1 g of silver chloride is washed with 250 ml of water at 25 °C: $K_{sp} = [Ag^+] [Cl^-] =$ 1.56×10^{-10} mole^2 . l.$^{-2}$. If a moles of silver chloride dissolve in 1 litre of water, then $[Ag^+] = [Cl^-] = a$, since on dissolution of one mole of silver chloride, one mole of chloride and one mole of silver ions are produced. Substituting into the expression for K_{sp}, we have $K_{sp} = a^2 = 1.56 \times 10^{-10}$ mole^2 . l.$^{-2}$, and obtain $a = \sqrt{1.56 \times 10^{-10}}$ mole . l.$^{-1} =$ $= 1.25 \times 10^{-5}$ mole . l.$^{-1}$.

The concentration of silver chloride in g/l is then obtained by multiplying a by the gram formula weight of silver chloride: 1.25×10^{-5} mole . l.$^{-1} \times 143.3$ g . mole$^{-1} =$ $= 1.8 \times 10^{-3}$ g/l. Therefore, only 4.5×10^{-4} g of silver chloride will dissolve in the 250 ml of water used. The relative error is not very small, being $\frac{4.5 \times 10^{-4} \times 100}{0.1} \% = 0.45\%$.

It is even easier to calculate the error which is caused in the gravimetric determination of 0.1 g of silver chloride by washing the precipitate with 0.01 M hydrochloric acid. In this case $[Cl^-] = 10^{-2}$ mole . l.$^{-1}$. Neglecting, in comparison with this, the chloride ion concentration which would be caused by the dissolution of silver chloride, we obtain $[Ag^+] = \frac{K_{sp}}{[Cl^-]} = \frac{1.56 \times 10^{-10} \text{mole}^2 . \text{l.}^{-2}}{1 \times 10^{-2} \text{mole} . \text{l.}^{-1}} = 1.56 \times 10^{-8}$ mole . l.$^{-1}$, corresponding to 2.24×10^{-6} g/l for the solubility of the silver chloride: therefore 5.6×10^{-5} g of silver chloride dissolve in the 250 ml of acid used. In this case the relative error is $\frac{5.6 \times 10^{-5} \times 100}{0.1} \% = 0.056\%$. This value can be neglected even in precise analysis. Moreover, it must be considered that in practice the equilibrium is never completely established between the wash-liquid and precipitate, so that the actual error is even smaller than the calculated one.

It is evident from these calculations, how important an excess of precipitant is for the quantitative precipitation of the precipitate, though too

Table 3.5. Solubility Products of some Insoluble Inorganic
Compounds (20 °C)

Compound	K_{sp}	Compound	K_{sp}
Halides		*Carbonates*	
AgCl	1×10^{-10}	*and Oxalates*	
AgBr	6×10^{-13}	$MgCO_3$	2×10^{-4}
AgI	1×10^{-16}	$CaCO_3$	1×10^{-8}
AgSCN	1×10^{-12}	$BaCO_3$	7×10^{-9}
$PbCl_2$	2×10^{-5}	$SrCO_3$	2×10^{-9}
CuSCN	2×10^{-11}	BaC_2O_4	2×10^{-7}
		SrC_2O_4	6×10^{-8}
Hydroxides		CaC_2O_4	2×10^{-9}
$Fe(OH)_3$	1×10^{-36}		
$Al(OH)_3$	8×10^{-32}	*Chromates*	
$Zn(OH)_2$	1×10^{-17}	Ag_2CrO_4	2×10^{-12}
$Ni(OH)_2$	1×10^{-16}	$Ag_2Cr_2O^7$	2×10^{-7}
$Ca(OH)_2$	1×10^{-16}	$BaCrO_4$	2×10^{-10}
$Mn(OH)_2$	1×10^{-12}	$PbCrO_4$	2×10^{-14}
$Mg(OH)_2$	2×10^{-9}		
		Sulphides	
Sulphates		Ag_2S	10^{-50}
$CaSO_4$	6×10^{-5}	HgS	10^{-53}
$SrSO_4$	3×10^{-7}	ZnS	10^{-25}
$BaSO_4$	1×10^{-10}	CdS	10^{-27}
$PbSO_4$	1×10^{-8}	PbS	10^{-28}
		Bi_2S_3	10^{-91}

large an excess must be avoided if co-precipitation is likely to occur or the precipitant can form a soluble complex with the precipitate.

Another calculation, also very useful in practice, permits determination of the concentration of the wash-liquid needed to make the precipitate practically completely insoluble.

Suppose for example, a precipitate of calcium oxalate monohydrate is to be washed, and not more than 10^{-8} mole of calcium is to be dissolved from the precipitate by 300 ml of wash-liquid. The solubility product of calcium oxalate is $K_{sp} = [Ca^{2+}] [(COO)_2^{2-}] = 2 \times 10^{-9}$ mole^2 . 1^{-2}. Substituting 10^{-8} mole . 1^{-1} for Ca^{2+}, we obtain $[(COO)_2^{2-}] = \dfrac{2 \times 10^{-9} \text{ mole}^2 . 1^{-2}}{10^{-8} \text{ mole} . 1^{-1}} = 2 \times 10^{-1}$ mole . 1^{-1}. If the precipitate were to be washed with 1 litre of washing liquid, we would have to use 0.2M ammonium oxalate. Since, however, we are to use only 300 ml of the wash-liquid, then only a maximum of 0.3×10^{-8} moles of calcium would be dissolved by this solution, and we need use a solution only a third as concentrated, i.e. 0.06M, corresponding roughly to 1% w/v ammonium oxalate solution.

Other factors besides solubility in water must be taken into account in discussing completeness of precipitation. Almost all precipitating anions are strong bases, and the effect of the pH of solution must be considered. For example, take the situation in which a metal ion A^{n+} is precipitated by the anion B^- of a weak monobasic acid HB.

$$K_{sp} = [A] [B]^n; \qquad BH \rightleftharpoons H^+ + B^-; \qquad K = \frac{[H] [B]}{[HB]}$$

Then the fraction Φ_B of total reagent concentration C_B that is in the form B^- is given by

$$\Phi_B = \frac{[B]}{[B] + [HB]} = \frac{[B]}{[B]\{1 + [H]/K\}} \tag{3.21}$$

$$= \frac{K}{K + [H]} \tag{3.22}$$

If S is the molar solubility of the precipitate, then at equilibrium in aqueous medium, $[A] = s$, and $[B] = ns$; but if the wash solution is sufficiently acid for B to be protonated, more precipitate will have to dissolve in order to maintain the ion product K_{sp} constant. If this actual solubility is s', then

$$[A][B]^n = s'(ns'\Phi_B)^n = K_{sp} \tag{3.23}$$

and

$$s' = \left(\frac{K_{sp}}{n^n \Phi_B^n}\right)^{\frac{1}{(n+1)}} \tag{3.24}$$

A similar argument applies to precipitates containing anions derived from dibasic and tribasic acids, but here Φ_B will be

$$\frac{K_1 K_2}{[H]^2 + [H]K_1 + K_1 K_2} \quad \text{and} \quad \frac{K_1 K_2 K_3}{[H]^3 + K_1[H]^2 + K_1 K_2[H] + K_1 K_2 K_3}$$

respectively.

Turning now to the cation, we shall expect the precipitate to dissolve if a reagent is present that can form complexes with the cation, e.g.

$$A + nX \rightleftharpoons AX_n; \qquad K = \frac{[AX_n]}{[A][X]^n} \tag{[3.25}$$

Then the fraction Φ_A of the total concentration of A in solution as free cation will be

$$\Phi_A = \frac{[A]}{[A] + [AX] + - - - [AX_n]} =$$

$$= \frac{1}{1 + k_1[X] + k_1 k_2[X]^2 + - - - k_1 k_2 k_n[X]^n} \tag{3.26}$$

where k_1 etc. are the stepwise formation constants of AX, AX_2, etc., and if s' is the actual molar solubility of the precipitate in the presence of X then

$$[A][B]^n = s'\Phi_A(ns')^n = K_{sp}$$

and

$$s = \left(\frac{K_{sp}}{n^n \Phi_A}\right)^{\frac{n}{(n+1)}} \tag{3.27}$$

If X is itself the anion of a weak acid, with dissociation constant K_x, then the solubility will be affected by pH, and we shall have, for the case where both B and X may be protonated

$$\Phi_A' = \frac{1}{1 + k_1[X'] + k_1 k_2[X']^2 + - - -} \tag{3.28}$$

where

$$[X'] = \frac{([X] + [HX]) K_x}{K_x + [H]} \cdot$$

Then

$$[A] [B]^n = s' \Phi'_A (ns' \Phi_B)^n = K_{sp}$$

or

$$s' = \left(\frac{K_{sp}}{n^n \Phi_B^n \Phi'_A} \right)^{\frac{1}{(n+1)}} \qquad (3.29)$$

An alternative approach is to use Ringbom's α-coefficients for the side-reactions of protonation of the precipitating anion and of complexation of metal ion. If we denote by $\alpha_{(HB)}$ the ratio of the overall concentration of the anion (irrespective of species) to the concentration of free anion, we have

$$\alpha_{(HB)} = \frac{[H_nB] + [H_{n-1}B] + - - - - + [B]}{[B]} \qquad (3.30)$$

and

$$[A] [B]^n = s'(ns')^n / \alpha_{(HB)} = K_{sp} \qquad (3.31)$$

a result analogous to that obtained in Eq. 3.23, except that $\alpha_{(HB)}$ is the inverse of Φ_B. Similarly, Eq. 3.27 will become

$$s' = \left(\frac{K_{sp} \alpha_{(Ax)}}{n^n} \right)^{\frac{1}{(n+1)}} \qquad (3.32)$$

where $\alpha_{(Ax)}$ is the inverse of Φ_A (Eq. 3.26).

The solubility product is also used for error calculations in precipitation titrations in which the equivalence point may be indicated by the formation of a sparingly soluble precipitate with the excess of titrant, and in complexometric titrations in which a precipitate is redissolved.

For example, in the Mohr titration silver nitrate solution is added to sodium chloride solution to which potassium chromate solution has been added. Silver chloride is precipitated preferentially in the course of the titration, but as soon as the chloride concentration falls to a certain value red-brown silver chromate forms, indicating the equivalence point. The amount of chloride ions not titrated corresponds to the silver ion concentration at which the silver chromate forms. This untitrated amount can be determined from the solubility product $K_{Ag_2CrO_4} = [Ag^+]^2 [CrO_4^{2-}] = 2 \times 10^{-12}$ mole³. 1⁻³, by calculating the chromate ion concentration in the solution and substituting this value into the equation. If we consider the case in which 1 ml of 5% w/v potassium chromate solution has been added to a mixture of 25 ml each of 0.1 M sodium chloride and 0.1 M silver nitrate, the chromate ion concentration is $[CrO_4^{2-}] = \frac{0.05}{194.2} \times \frac{1000}{50}$ mole . 1⁻¹ $= 5.15 \times 10^{-3}$ mole . 1⁻¹. Then the chloride ion concentration not titrated is equal to the silver ion concentration, which is given by

$$[Ag^+] = \sqrt{\frac{2 \times 10^{-12}}{5.15 \times 10^{-3}}} \text{ mole . } 1^{-1} \approx 2 \times 10^{-2} \text{ mole . } 1^{-1}$$

The amount of chloride untitrated is $\frac{50}{1\,000} \times 2 \times 10^{-5}$ mole $= 10^{-6}$ mole; the amount taken was $\frac{25}{1\,000} \times 0.1$ mole, so the error is $\frac{10^{-6} \times 100}{2.5 \times 10^{-3}}$ %, or 0.04%.

It can be seen from the calculation that in this case the titration error depends on the concentration of the indicator added; this is to be expected, considering that the indicator also plays the role of a precipitant. If too much chromate is added to the solution, silver chromate is formed before the equivalence point has been reached; on the other hand, if the chromate concentration is too small, an excess of silver nitrate must be added to the solution, and moreover the colour of the silver chromate formed will be less distinct. The most favourable indicator concentration is best determined empirically. If the titrant is standardized by titration of pure sodium chloride it is recommended that the titration conditions (amount of indicator, concentrations and volumes of solutions, etc.) should be kept as nearly as possible the same as those for the subsequent use of the titrant in determinations. In this way a correction of the titration error is included, to a certain extent, in the titre itself. Ammonium ions interfere in this titration and the best conditions can be calculated by means of α-coefficients [95a] or a computer programme [37a].

In precipitation titrations in which the end-point is detected by means of adsorption indicators or by physical methods, we can apply similar arguments to those used in discussing gravimetric procedures, but now the value of K_{sp} becomes more critical because we can no longer use the common ion effect to increase the completeness of precipitation. The error arising from the solubility of the precipitate is now readily calculated from the solubility product — for a precipitate AB_n, the error at the equivalence point of a titration of m ml of an xM solution of A with t ml of B is

$$\frac{100(m + t)}{mx} \left(\frac{K_{sp}}{n^n}\right)^{\frac{1}{(n+1)}} \% \qquad (3.33)$$

The effect of pH and of complex formation will, of course, be more marked because of the absence of the common ion effect.

3.6 Titration error of oxidation-reduction titrations

The titration error of redox titrations is calculated, in principle, similarly to the titration errors of neutralization, precipitation and complex-formation titrations already discussed; the calculation is based on determining the amount of substance that remains untitrated at the end-point marked by the indicator, or on determining the amount of volumetric solution which has to be added at the equivalence point for the colour change to take place. In carrying out these calculations for redox titrations we always set out from the *Nernst equation*

$$E = E^0 + \frac{RT}{nF} \cdot \ln K \qquad [(3.34)$$

where K is the equilibrium constant, E^0 the standard potential in V, T the temperature in °K, R the gas constant (8.3144 abs. joules/deg. mole = 1.9872 cal/deg. mole) and F the Faraday, i.e. 96494 coulombs. For oxidation reactions, described by the relation $Red = Ox + ne^-$ where Red is the reduced and Ox the oxidized form of the same substance and n the number of electrons exchanged in the reaction, the Nernst equation takes the form

$$E = E^0 + \frac{RT}{nF} \cdot \ln \frac{[Ox]}{[Red]} = E^0 + 2.303 \cdot \frac{RT}{nF} \log \frac{[Ox]}{[Red]} \qquad (3.35)$$

According to this, the redox potential E (i.e. the potential which is established on a bright platinum electrode, immersed in the solution in which the redox reaction takes place) depends first of all on the value of the standard redox potential E^0 which represents the redox potential at $[Ox] = [Red]$ and is a characteristic constant for every electrochemical reaction. The quantity E is usually called the *formal redox potential* if $[Ox]$ and $[Red]$ are expressed as concentrations. The values of standard potentials of some reactions used frequently in practical analysis have been tabulated [31]. The redox potential depends, moreover, on the ratio of the concentrations $[Ox]$ and $[Red]$ (but not on their absolute values) and on the temperature. The value of the expression $2.303\ RT/F$ at $t\ °C$ is $(0.0541 + 0.0002t)$ V per equivalent; at room temperature (about 25 °C) the value of 0.06 V per equivalent is often used for approximate calculations.

In redox titrations we must always have a system of at least two interacting redox reactions, e.g. in oxidimetric titrations:

$Red_1 \rightarrow Ox_1 + n_1 e^-$ (substance to be determined, standard potential E_1^0)

$Red_2 \rightarrow Ox_2 + n_2 e^-$ (titrant; standard potential E_2^0)

$n_2 Red_1 + n_1 Ox_2 \rightarrow n_2 Ox_1 + n_1 Red_2$.

The potential of the entire reaction is $E = E_1^0 - E_2^0$. If the redox reaction is to be quantitative, the values of the standard potentials E_1^0 and E_2^0 must be sufficiently far apart. For example $MnO_4^- + 8H^+ + 5e^- \rightarrow Mn^{2+} + 4H_2O$; $E^0 = +1.5$ V: $Fe^{3+} + e \rightarrow Fe^{2+}$; $E^0 = 0.76$ V, and for the reaction

$$MnO_4^- + 5\,Fe^{2+} + 8\,H^+ \rightarrow Mn^{2+} + 5\,Fe^{3+} + 4\,H_2O, \quad E = 0.74\,V,$$

which is rather a high value. Compared to this, the reaction

$$2\,Fe^{3+} + 2\,I^- \rightarrow I_2 + 2\,Fe^{2+}$$

would not be quantitative, as $E_{Fe^{3+}/Fe^{2+}}^0 = +0.76\,V$ and $E_{\frac{1}{2}I_2/I}^0 = +0.58\,V$ result in a value of $E = 0.18$ V, so that K for the reaction corresponds to about 95 % oxidation.

Let us now investigate the calculation of the change in redox potential in the course of the titration. Before the equivalence point has been reached $[Ox_2]$ is very small and we shall have $E = E^0 + \frac{RT}{n_1 F} \ln \frac{[Ox_1]}{[Red_1]}$, and after the equivalence point has been passed $[Red_1]$ becomes negligibly small and we have

$$E = E_2^0 + \frac{RT}{n_2 F} \ln \frac{[Red_2]}{[Ox_2]}.$$

Precisely at the equivalence point the potential is $E_T = \dfrac{n_1 E_1^0 + n_2 E_2^0}{n_1 + n_2}$.

This formula is used in conjunction with the Nernst equation to determine the amount of Red_1 titrated, or the amount of Ox_2 added in excess at the indicated end-point. As redox indicators themselves are substances capable of being reduced or oxidized at a certain potential, and their two forms I_{red} and I_{ox} differ in colour, the human eye is capable of distinguishing the colour change, as with neutralization indicators and two-colour complexometric indicators, only over the range from $\dfrac{[I_{ox}]}{[I_{red}]} = \dfrac{90}{10}$ to $\dfrac{[I_{ox}]}{[I_{red}]} = \dfrac{10}{90}$,

the potential limits of the colour change being from $E_I^0 + \dfrac{RT}{nF} \cdot \ln 9$ to $E_I^0 - \dfrac{RT}{nF} \cdot \ln 9$, i.e. $E_I^0 \pm \dfrac{0.06}{n}$ V.

In the case of many redox indicators frequently used in practice, the whole situation is further complicated by the fact that their colour change is also influenced by the proton dissociation $HI_{ox} \rightarrow I_{red}^- + H^+$: the overall potential then is $E = E_I^0 + \dfrac{RF}{nF} \cdot \ln \dfrac{[I_{red}]}{[HI_{ox}]} + \dfrac{RT}{nF} \ln [H^+]$, from which it can be seen that the potential for the colour change decreases by 0.06 V per unit increase in pH. Some redox indicators and their standard potentials are given in Table 3.6. Fortunately most redox titrations are carried out in acid medium at pH 1.0 or less, and in this region of acidity the effect of pH on the indicator potential can be ignored.

Table 3.6. Standard Potentials of some Redox Indicators

Indicator	$E_I^0(pH = 0)$
Indigo monosulphonate	0.26 V
Indigo tetrasulphonate	0.36 V
Methylene blue	0.53 V
Diphenylamine	0.76 V
Diphenylsulphonic acid	0.85 V
Erioglaucine	1.00 V
Iron(II)-o-phenanthroline complex	1.14 V
Iron(II)-o-nitrophenanthroline complex	1.25 V

Let us now determine the titration error for iron(II) titrated with cerium(IV) sulphate ($E^0_{Ce^{4+}/Ce^{3+}} = +1.44$ V). The potential at the equivalence point is

$$E_T = \frac{0.76 + 1.44}{2} \text{ V} = 1.10 \text{ V}.$$

If erioglaucine is used as indicator ($E_I^0 = 1.00$ V) the colour change will begin at $E = (1.0 - 0.06)$ V $= 0.94$ V and be "complete" at 1.06 V, i.e. before the equivalence point. The end-point is seen when the colour change is complete. The concentration of the iron (II) not titrated is then determined as follows:

$$E = E^0 + 0.06 \log \frac{[Fe^{3+}]}{[Fe^{2+}]}; \qquad 1.06 = 0.76 + 0.06 \log \frac{[Fe^{3+}]}{[Fe^{2+}]},$$

so

$$\log \frac{[Fe^{3+}]}{[Fe^{2+}]} = 5.0 \quad \text{and} \quad [Fe^{3+}] = 10^5 \times [Fe^{2+}],$$

so that the relative error ε is $10^2/10^5\,\% = 0.001\,\%$.

When the titration is carried out with the 5-nitro-1,10-phenanthroline iron (II) complex as indicator ($E_r^0 = 1.25$ V) the colour change is "complete" at a potential of $E = (1.25 + 0.06)$ V $= 1.31$ V, i.e. only after the equivalence point has been passed. The error is calculated as follows:

$$1.31 = 1.44 + 0.06 \log \frac{[Ce^{4+}]}{[Ce^{3+}]}, \quad \text{so} \quad \log \frac{[Ce^{3+}]}{[Ce^{4+}]} = 2.16,$$

and therefore $[Ce^{3+}] = 150\,[Ce^{4+}]$. The excess of cerium(IV) sulphate solution added at the end-point gives the relative error $\varepsilon = \dfrac{100}{150}\,\% = 0.7\,\%$.

It should be mentioned, however, that these calculations do not reflect the real situation completely, as on the one hand the dependence on pH is not considered, and on the other it is not taken into account that redox indicators may not react reversibly, and that the rate of establishment of equilibrium (and therefore the practicability of redox titrations) is influenced by the presence of certain catalysts. For these reasons calculations of this type should only be regarded as a first approximation to the answer to the problem.

3.7 Errors of electrometric titrations

Electrometric titration is used for neutralization, precipitation, complexometric and redox titrations, in which the equivalence point is indicated not by the colour change of an indicator, but by measurement of certain electrochemical properties of the reaction mixture, which are related to the concentration either of the substance to be determined or of the titrant. For example, in *potentiometric titrations* the potential difference is measured between the indicator electrode and a reference electrode or between two indicating electrodes, or between two similar electrodes one of which acts as indication electrode and the other is immersed in a reference solution already at the desired equivalence point and serves as reference electrode. Another type of electrometric titration is *amperometric titration* (polarographic titration), in which the current is measured between a reference and an indicating electrode, to which a selected voltage is applied. The indicating electrodes used are the dropping mercury electrode, or electrodes of platinum, gold, graphite etc. We may also use *dead-stop titrations*, in which a constant voltage is applied to two polarized electrodes of the same material and current flows only when one (or both) of the electrodes is (are) depolarized; the depolarization is arranged to occur at the equivalence point. In *conductometric titrations* the property used to detect the equivalence point is electrical conductivity. Of course, in electrometric titrations we cannot speak of "indicator errors", which have been defined in the preceding sections as errors caused by the difference between the true equivalence point and the end-point indicated by the colour change of the indicator. This, however, does not mean that electrometric titrations are not subject to error. Assuming some simplifications we find two principal causes of such errors in electrometric titrations.

1. The measuring system, by means of which the change of electrometric properties is being followed during the titration, may not react quickly enough for large concentration changes of the component to be determined, in the immediate vicinity of the equivalence point.

2. The measuring system, by means of which we determine the achievement of a certain value (e.g. the zero or maximum value) of the property in question at the equivalence point, indicates this value either before or after the equivalence point.

As an example of the first class of causes we may mention slow potential stabilization in potentiometric titrations, which easily leads to over-titration, because the measuring equipment reacts too late. Specially dangerous in this sense are partial polarization of the electrodes, or their covering by a precipitate. The second case may occur, for example, in dead-stop titrations. This also includes the case, where in potentiometric titrations with an auxiliary electrode immersed in an equivalent mixture, the potentials of the two electrodes differ somewhat at the actual equivalence point, because of slight differences in pH, ionic strength, electrodes, surface of the electrodes, or degree of polarization, causing the end of the titration to be indicated too late or too early.

Other sources of error of electrometric titration include side-reactions taking place on the electrode surfaces. For example, an antimony electrode cannot be used in solutions of acids which form stable complexes with antimony, a quinhydrone electrode cannot be used in solutions of high pH or containing ammonium ions, amino-acids or proteins. The hydrogen electrode is subject to salt and protein errors, which is one of the drawbacks of this electrode compared to the glass electrode. When electrodes covered with platinum black are used (e.g. the hydrogen electrode or electrodes used in conductometric titrations) some substances cause "poisoning" of the electrode. Reference electrodes can also cause difficulties in use of the chosen electrode system: e.g. silver chloride electrodes cannot be used in ammonia solutions or in the presence of veronal and of other complex-forming substances. Sometimes, unwanted electrode polarization may take place, e.g. in conductometry or in precipitation titrations, when substances not to be titrated are co-precipitated with the precipitate. This holds for potentiometric as well as polarographic indication.

Such influences of course cause systematic errors, which frequently may be removed by modifying the experimental conditions.

3.8 Purity of precipitates

Precipitates obtained in gravimetric analyses and precipitation titrations are generally not perfectly pure, containing usually other components of the solution beside the substance precipitated. Contamination of precipitates with substances which are otherwise soluble under the conditions of precipitation used, is called co-precipitation. The mechanism of such co-precipitation may differ. Sometimes it is simple adsorption on the surface, components of the solution accumulating on the surface of the precipitate where they achieve a concentration larger than in the surrounding solution; such components are bound by the precipitate and can be removed from the surface more or less easily by washing. In other cases the forces holding the impurities to the precipitate surface — especially in the case of crystalline precipitates — are rather of electrostatic character, due to the influence of ions located in the upper layers of the crystal lattice; here we speak of lattice-type surface effects. Another effect is the formation of isomorphous mixed crystals, which however may be expected only if the solution contains ions of the same charge and approximately the same effective radius as the precipitated ions.

Double salts sometimes form in a similar way; in other cases, precipitate nuclei, contaminated with adsorbed solution components, agglomerate to form larger particles, so that impurities find their way even into these particles and cannot be removed by washing. This type of contamination is called occlusion. When successive precipitation, e.g. of two anions by a single cation, should take place according to the respective solubility products, mixed crystals sometimes form and separation is imperfect. Sometimes we may also observe an effect called induced precipitation; the example most frequently used is the precipitation of zinc sulphide together with mercuric sulphide, even from a strongly acid medium, sometimes in large amounts. We shall later discuss the great significance of co-precipitation. Contamination of precipitates is not associated with adsorption or occlusion alone; usually several influences act together in precipitation to cause contamination of the precipitate; only occasionally may it be assumed that one mechanism will predominate over others.

The composition of the solid and liquid phase on precipitation of a crystalline ionic precipitate is characterized by the CHLOPIN distribution coefficient [45] $D = \dfrac{x(1 - y)}{y(1 - x)}$ where x and y are the ratios of the co-precipitated and precipitated components in the precipitate to the overall amount of these components respectively. Chlopin assumed that when the precipitate is being formed, ions of the precipitated and co-precipitated components are in equilibrium with the ions in the solution, and that thus the distribution of the admixture in the crystal is homogeneous. DOERNER and HOSKINS [49] set out from kinetic views, defining the logarithmic distribution coefficient $\log \dfrac{b}{b - x} = \lambda \log \dfrac{a}{a - x}$, a and b being the initial concentrations of the precipitated and co-precipitated components respectively. When $\lambda > 1$, the precipitate is enriched with the contaminant as compared to the solution; when $\lambda < 1$ it is poorer. Doerner and Hoskins [49] assume that recrystallization and solid phase diffusion are negligible and that equilibrium is established only between the solution and the newly forming layer of the crystal lattice. According to their views, the impurity in the precipitate may be distributed inhomogeneously.

Adsorption takes place according to the Freundlich relation in dependence on the concentration of impurities in the solution and on the amount of the precipitate:

$$\frac{x}{m} = kc^n \tag{3.36}$$

Here x denotes the amount of impurities bound by the mass of the precipitate m, the concentration of impurities remaining in the solution is $c = \dfrac{a - x}{v}$, a being the initial amount of impurity in a volume v; k and n are empirical constants.

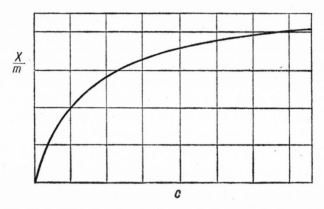

FIG. 3.2. The Freundlich adsorption isotherm; c is the concentration of the adsorbed substance in the solution, x is the amount of this substance co-precipitated on a mass m of precipitate.

The graphical expression of this relation is the Freundlich adsorption isotherm (Fig. 3.2). From this isotherm follows the important result, that adsorption is the greater, the greater the concentration of adsorbed substances in the solution from which precipitation is made. It is known from practice that different substances are co-precipitated with different readiness. This is largely due to the rule that the precipitate is contaminated most by the least soluble components of the solution, and this is a consequence of the Gibbs equation

$$\Gamma = -\frac{c}{RT} \cdot \frac{\mathrm{d}\gamma}{\mathrm{d}c} \tag{3.37}$$

In this equation Γ denotes the surface concentration of the absorbed substance, γ the surface tension, R the gas constant, T the absolute temperature, and c has the same significance as in the preceding relation. If $\dfrac{\mathrm{d}\gamma}{\mathrm{d}c}$ is negative, the right-hand side of the equation becomes positive and the surface is positive. Thus only those substances accumulate on the surface of the precipitate, which give a decrease of surface tension with rising concentration.

Electrostatic adsorption (the lattice surface effect) becomes effective mainly with crystalline precipitates and is sometimes manifested by co-precipitation of the precipitating agent. For example, in the precipitation of chloride ions by silver nitrate solution, the precipitating silver chloride adsorbs chloride ions that have not yet been precipitated, but as soon as these ions disappear when precipitation has been completed, any excess of silver ions begins to be adsorbed and co-precipitated. For gravimetric analysis co-precipitation is a source of grave error; in order to achieve quantitative precipitation, an excess of the precipitant must be used, and the greater this excess, the higher the degree of co-precipitation of the precipitant [30]. This explains the requirement that only a slight excess of the precipitant should be added. In other cases of course we intentionally achieve co-precipitation of a certain amount of the precipitant in order to compensate the partial solubility of the precipitate, e.g. the Hintz-Weber method of sulphate determination. The compensation of errors of gravimetric analysis is discussed for example by SCHRÖER [89].

Another phenomenon which has an unfavourable effect, for example on the argentometric determination of chloride and bromide ions in the presence of each other, is the formation of mixed crystals. This may be explained by the course of the equilibrium $AgBr + Cl^- \rightleftarrows AgCl + Br^-$, the silver chloride which is being formed dissolving in silver bromide. In the course of the titration silver chloride is co-precipitated with the bromide at an increasing rate, because the concentration of the bromide ions decreases far more quickly than that of the chloride ions, and the reaction equilibrium shifts in the direction indicated. When wishing to determine the distribution coefficient D for the distribution of individual ions between the precipitate and the solution, we employ the relation $D = \dfrac{N_{Cl} \cdot [Br^-]}{N_{Br} \cdot [Cl^-]}$, N_{Cl}, B_{Br} being the molar fractions of the ions in the precipitate and $[Cl^-]$, $[Br^-]$ their concentrations in the solution. KOLTHOFF et al. [20] have determined a value of $D = 393$ for the case of chlorides and bromides. From this the relative error of "co-precipitation" of chlorides with silver bromide may be calculated by use of the relation $\dfrac{a - x}{x} = \sqrt{D}$ where a and x are the number of moles of bromide and chloride respectively. Assuming $a = 100\%$ and knowing that $D = 393$, we obtain directly the mole per cent of chloride precipitated together with the bromide, i.e. $x = 4.8\%$. In practice we may sometimes avoid the formation of mixed crystals by increasing the ionic strength of the solution by addition of a neutral electrolyte, e.g. aluminium sulphate.

In gravimetric analysis the purity of the precipitate and the quantitativeness of precipitation are the most important prerequisites of accurate results, and for this reason a large number of studies has been devoted to these problems. In principle we always try to obtain the purest precipitate possible; if this is not possible, the precipitate must be additionally purified.

To obtain precipitates of highest purity, different procedures are recommended in individual cases. Perhaps the most general, and in practice best proved, view has been expressed by HOVORKA [18], that if an amorphous precipitate is formed, it is best precipitated from a small volume by a concentrated precipitant solution, while in the formation of a crystalline precipitate it is better to let it form gradually from a large volume with a dilute precipitant solution. In cases where the same compound can be obtained with different precipitants, the purity of the precipitate will depend on the agent used: e.g. a precipitate of iron(III) hydroxide is usually purer if it is obtained with a pyridine solution than if it is precipitated with ammonia, etc. The particle size is also not devoid of influence on the purity of the precipitate: smaller particles, especially in an amorphous precipitate, have a larger surface and therefore adsorb more impurities. On the other hand, with crystalline precipitates it is not always best for unduly large crystals to be formed, since they may easily occlude the mother liquor. The particle size depends mainly, as shown by VON WEIMARN [96], on the rate of precipitation; the slower the precipitate is formed from the solution, the larger its particles. The rate of precipitation is given by the relation

$$V = K \cdot \frac{Q - S}{S} \tag{3.38}$$

where K is a constant characteristic for the given substance, Q is its actual concentration in the solution and S its solubility. Thus the rate of precipitation, with given values of K and S which are constants for a given precipitate, is mainly given by the degree of supersaturation $Q - S$. The greater this supersaturation, the more rapidly is a fine precipitate formed, while with low degrees of supersaturation a coarse-grained precipitate is slowly formed. From these results also follows the significance of slow addition of the precipitant and of efficient mixing.

Highly pure precipitates, especially if they are crystalline, are also obtained by *precipitation from homogeneous medium*. As we have seen, crystalline precipitates must be formed as slowly as possible. Two procedures are possible: either we add the precipitant and precipitate slowly by adjusting the pH value (e.g. by neutralizing the excess of acid) or we precipitate slowly by gradually adding the precipitant. Of course even slow neutralization always takes place at the end by a sudden change of pH (see e.g. the curve in Fig. 3.1) and even with good mixing we cannot avoid some degree of local concentration gradients of the precipitant added dropwise to the solution; thus we cannot avoid the formation of aggregates of precipitate particles which might occlude the mother liquor, or the adsorption of precipitant. If, however, an excess of urea is added to a sufficiently acid solution containing the precipitant (e.g. in the determination of calcium salts by oxalic acid), we obtain a clear, homogeneous solution; when the mixture is heated, urea decomposes according to the equation $CO(NH_2)_2 + 2H^+ \rightarrow CO_2 + 2NH_4^+$, i.e. with simultaneous neutralization of the acid. The pH change takes place gradually, because with the decreasing concentration of hydrogen ions the course of the reaction is slowed down, and the precipitate separates very slowly in a form easily filtered off. In other cases again, a substance may be added which when slowly heated decomposes to liberate the precipitant uniformly throughout the solution, e.g. triethylphosphate or trimethylphosphate in the precipitation of phosphates, dimethyl sulphate or sulphamic acid in the precipitation of sulphates, etc. In this case again the formation of the precipitate takes place very slowly, and in particular the precipitant is formed throughout the entire solution homogeneously, without any local concentration variations and formation of aggregates of precipitate particles; the method has been worked out by GORDON, SALUTSKY and WILLARD [11]. In other methods metal ions may be released from complexes by oxidation of the ligand, change of pH, etc.

The form of the precipitate is important for the correct course of filtration; the more coarse-grained it is, the more easily is it filtered off and washed. A source of grave error may be the formation of colloidal precipitates, e.g. some hydroxides [$Fe(OH)_3$, $Al(OH)_3$ etc.]; these generally form if the reaction mixture or the washing water do not contain a sufficient amount of electrolytes (so-called peptization of the precipitate).

The precipitate obtained must always be washed in order to remove mother liquor. TREADWELL [33] mentions a relation for the calculation of the electrolyte concentration retained by the precipitate, following from the Ostwald dilution law:

$$c_n = \left(\frac{R}{V+R}\right)^n . c.$$

(3.39)

where c_n is the electrolyte concentration in the precipitate after the nth washing, c is the electrolyte concentration in the solution from which the precipitate has been obtained, V is the liquid volume used for each washing and R is the liquid volume retained by the precipitate. This relation is of no practical significance for the calculation of the actual contamination of the precipitate, since it is derived under the assumption that no adsorption takes place on the precipitate; some conclusions follow from it, however, which are important for a correct washing procedure. First of all the precipitate is the purer, the smaller the concentration of impurities in the solution from which the precipitate has been obtained, a fact which after all also follows from the Freundlich isotherm. Obviously, the greater the volume of the precipitate on the filter, the greater R will be, and the slower the process of washing out the impurities; in other words more voluminous precipitates must be washed more thoroughly. We see furthermore that it is more advantageous to wash several times with smaller volumes of the washing solution, than to wash only once with a large volume, and finally that the washing liquid must be allowed to drain entirely before the washing operation is repeated (with the exception, of course, of some sulphides which might become oxidized on exposure to air). A practical test should always be carried out with a filtrate sample to make sure that washing is complete.

Decantation, washing and sometimes even digestion do not always lead to perfect removal of the impurities from the precipitate; e.g. if the impurities are occluded, reprecipitation is always necessary ("double precipitation"), i.e. the precipitate must be dissolved and precipitated anew.

Classical gravimetry knew quite a number of special methods for the purification of precipitates; e.g. the purification of stannic acid by fusion with sodium carbonate and sulphur (the "Freiberg" method), and volatilization of "raw" silicic acid with hydrofluoric acid, which is not purification in the true sense of the word, but an operation which allows the true value of pure silicon dioxide to be determined.

3.9 The temperature of drying and igniting precipitates

The precipitated and washed precipitate must be converted into a substance of constant composition and suitable properties to allow it to be weighed precisely and the [true content of the component sought to be determined from the mass of the precipitate. In practice we achieve a constant composition nearly always by the effect of elevated temperature: sometimes drying at $100-110$ °C suffices, in other cases the precipitate must be ignited. The duration and temperature of ignition depend on the properties, composition and amount of the substance ignited; the use of too low, as well as too high a temperature may lead to products of non-constant composition, either because the process in question did not continue to completion, or on the contrary, because further decomposition had already set in. The approximate temperatures of drying and ignition of various compounds occurring most frequently in gravimetric analysis are given by HOVORKA [18].

We are sometimes faced with the problem of selecting the most favourable form for weighing. Today the concept of converting substances into their final product of thermal decomposition is losing ground if such a product has some properties which make it unsuitable for weighing. Today we no longer ignite calcium oxalate to calcium oxide, which is rather hygroscopic, nor do we convert it into calcium sulphate, which is rather a lengthy operation; instead we ignite at $450-500$ °C to form calcium carbonate, carefully controlling the furnace temperature used for the ignition process. A very valuable aid to determining the suitable ignition temperature is thermogravimetry, perfected by DUVAL [9]. Another source of error may be the weighing of hygroscopic substances, weighing imperfectly cooled or moisture-absorbing crucibles with the precipitate, etc. We have, however, discussed these influences already in connection with the errors of weighing. Here it should also be noted that the time of 30 minutes sometimes stated as the time needed for cooling a crucible in a desiccator, is too short, especially if the crucible is made of porcelain.

Today, however, analysts are in some cases rid of the worry of achieving constant composition and constant weight of precipitates, and even of the purity of the precipitates, and there only remains the need to obtain complete precipitation of the entire amount of the component in question; such is the case with a procedure in which the washed precipitate is dissolved and the component sought is determined by titration. In this respect great possibilities are offered by complexometric methods in particular.

The errors of gravimetric analyses have been discussed comprehensively [52].

3.10 Errors of photometric determinations

Colorimetric and spectrophotometric measurement of the concentration of coloured substances is based on the validity of the LAMBERT-BEER law

$$A = k \cdot s \cdot c \tag{3.40}$$

where k is the absorptivity and s is the thickness of the solution layer. Thus there is a linear relation between the absorbance A and the concentration c, for a constant layer thickness of the solution. In practice, measurements disclose numerous deviations from this law, which holds best for dilute solutions.

Deviations from the Lambert-Beer law are usually classified as apparent and actual. *Apparent deviations* originate, in principle, from imperfections of the measuring equipment, while *true deviations* are caused by changes of the concentration of the light-absorbing substance.

Let us first discuss the *apparent deviations;* the extinction coefficient k of the Lambert-Beer law [21] always holds only for light of a given wavelength, while in practice we always measure with light of a range of wavelengths $\Delta\lambda$. When a spectrophotometer is being used, it is usually possible to select a sufficiently narrow spectral range, so that deviations caused by imperfectly monochromatic light will not attain great magnitude; we may frequently assume, at least approximately, that for the wavelength range employed the value of $dA/d\lambda$ is negligibly small, in other words that the absorptivity is in this case a constant independent of c and s. This assumption however is not fulfilled in colorimetry, where the light transmitted into the instrument by the filters includes one prevailing wavelength, corresponding to the so-called optical centre of the filter, while the other wavelengths of lower intensity are distributed around this centre. In this case the linear relation between A and c is not satisfied, and the value of the absorptivity cannot be regarded as a constant. In this case k is called the apparent absorptivity. Deviations from the Lambert-Beer law, resulting from imperfectly monochromatic light, are in principle caused by the different values of the absorptivity corresponding to the different wavelengths of light employed, in other words the deviations depend on the absorption spectrum. The variation of source intensity with wavelengths is also of importance, and so is the spectral sensitivity of photocells, or of the eye if a subjective colorimeter is being used. On the other hand, the influence of the density and refractive index of the solution becomes apparent only with solutions of higher concentrations, so that in practical measurements these do not cause important deviations.

True deviations from the Lambert-Beer law consist, as already stated, in concentration changes of the substance sought, taking place owing to the establishment of chemical equilibrium under the influence of inter-molecular and interionic forces, sometimes also by variations of the concentration ratio of coloured and colourless components of the solution analysed. Interionic forces participate mainly by the electrostatic field of ions of either the light-absorbing substance, or of the other electrolytes. The influence of foreign electrolytes, sometimes referred to as the "salt error", is mainly explained by the dependence of the activity coefficient of the coloured substance on the ionic strength $\lambda = \frac{1}{2} \Sigma c \cdot z^2$, where c is the molar concentration and z the charge of the ion. A similar influence is also exerted by polymeric substances; if these are e.g. proteins, we sometimes speak of the "protein error". Errors caused by dissociation of the coloured substance are mainly manifested in the measurement of coloured complexes of low stability, which are more or less strongly dissociated. Another source of error may be polymerization of compounds in the solution, e.g. dimerization of some dyes, etc.

It is clear from the discussion above, that true deviations from the Lambert-Beer law are mainly of importance with more concentrated solutions. This may be frequently observed when studying the dependence of A on c for a given colorimetric method, when above a certain concentration the law ceases to be valid, and a non-linear dependence of A on c appears.

We therefore do not always obtain a strictly linear relation between the measured absorbance and the concentration of the coloured substance, and it is usually necessary and always desirable to construct a calibration curve. The measurements used in constructing the calibration curve and for the determination proper must be carried out under the same conditions; in particular, the composition of solutions used for calibration should be the same as the composition of the sample solutions.

Details of errors will be found in a monograph by KORTÜM [21]. The validity of the Lambert-Beer law for some colorimetric methods has been studied by statistical means by GOTTSCHALK and DEHMEL [65].

3.11 Errors of emission spectrography

Emission spectrography is of great importance as a qualitative and semi-quantitative method allowing the simultaneous determination of a large number of elements. Under some conditions it is also a quantitative method. Qualitative emission spectrography is based on the fact that in atomic emission every element emits radiation of a characteristic wavelength. Quantitative spectrography is based on the principle that the relation between the intensity of monochromatic radiation I_λ incident on the detector (a photographic plate or a photomultiplier) and the concentration of the originating element in the plasma of the excitation source, c_x, is given by the LOMAKIN relation

$$I_\lambda = a \cdot c_x^b \tag{3.41a}$$

which is frequently used in the linear logarithmic form called the SCHEIBE-LOMAKIN equation

$$\log I = \log a + b \cdot \log c_x \tag{3.41b}$$

where a and b are constants. The constant b in the Scheibe-Lomakin relation represents the slope, being in fact the sensitivity of the spectral determination. In practice the Scheibe-Lomakin relation cannot be utilized directly. In semi-quantitative methods, spectra recorded on photographic plates are assessed by visual estimation, e.g. by comparing with a standard plate etc. These methods are usually characterized by great expedience, but they only permit determination of the concentration limits of the content of the element sought. The relative error of such semi-quantitative methods is generally around 20 %. In quantitative spectral analysis the results must also be assessed by comparison, because the degree of blackening of the lines on the plate is strongly influenced by many other circumstances beside the dependence on c_x, e.g. variations of the source, conditions of development of the plate etc. The degree of blackening of the spectral line is usually defined as

$$S = \log \frac{A}{A_0} = \log A - \log A_0 \tag{3.42}$$

where A_0 is the reading on the densitometer for the non-illuminated part of the plate in close vicinity to the line ("background"), and A is the reading for the spectral line. The quantitative determination is usually done according to GERLACH by means of the internal standard method, in which the blackening S_1 of the line of the element sought is compared to the blackening of the line of a basic element or of one added in a known and unvarying amount. This blackening of a certain line of the internal standard will be denoted by S_2. The difference $\Delta S = S_1 - S_2$ is then used as a measure of the concentration of the component to be determined. It is important that the difference of blackening ΔS should not be sensitive to variations of the excitation conditions [1]. For this reason it is essential that the internal standard be of approximately the same volatility as the element sought. For the excitation or ionization potential corresponding to the two lines to be roughly the same, it is favourable if the two lines have similar wavelengths and the elements have approximately the same atomic weight. The internal standard may be added only in such amounts that do not influence the other properties of the plasma. To eliminate, as far as possible, errors caused by variations of the arc temperature, so-called temperature regulators ("buffers") are added, such as alkali or alkaline earth metal salts or oxides. The comparison lines should also exhibit no self-absorption, i.e. decrease of blackening at high concentrations, due to absorption of the emitted radiation in the peripheral layers of the arc. It is clear that all these conditions can hardly be fulfilled simultaneously, especially if the same internal standard is being used for a number of elements. For this reason the graph of the relation between ΔS and c_x in the internal standard method frequently involves a set of points which can be encompassed with an ellipse, instead of a simple straight calibration line. Some details of this *"scatter" diagram*, according to HOLDT [67], will be given later. The variation of the results of spectral analysis is generally greater than with other analytical methods, but is usually of random character. Thus mathematical statistics, which are to be discussed in Chapter 4, are frequently used to evaluate the results of spectral analysis.

When searching for optimum conditions of the spectral determination of a certain element in a given type of material, a purely empirical procedure usually has to be employed. This holds — especially in spectral trace analysis — not only for the excitation conditions, amount of "buffers" etc., but also for preliminary operations, i.e. separation of the component to be determined from the matrix, etc. The question of whether separation has been done or whether the sample is being analysed just as it comes for analysis, with no preliminary chemical modification, is even important in the determination of the smallest possible amounts: if no separation has been done, we try to achieve the maximum relative sensitivity, i.e. maximum contrast between the line and the background. For this purpose instruments with high dispersion are suitable, and high contrast photographic plates are used, but excessively large samples and unnecessarily long exposures are unsuitable. When conventional chemical separation has been carried out, the highest possible absolute sensitivity must be strived for, and for this reason large samples and long exposures should be chosen and high-sensitivity photographic material is used. Separation methods suitable for use before spectral analysis are discussed in section 3.16.

3.12 Errors of flame photometry and atomic absorption photometry

Emission and absorption flame photometry have in common the feature that the solution to be analysed is sprayed into a flame, and for this reason the errors following from imperfections of the emitting or absorbing medium may be discussed jointly for the two methods. One source of error may be imperfect spraying (interfering transport effects) or the aerosol particles may evaporate incompletely, this being a frequent cause of non-linearity of the relation $M = f(c_x)$. In other cases, dissociation and association equilibria are established in the flame, or emitted radiation may be absorbed in the peripheral parts of the flame. Elimination of the interfering effects is frequently possible by a suitable method of assessing the results. Most of the interfering effects mentioned here arise from the composition of the solution analysed. Therefore, when the calibration curve is constructed, the standards used should always have the same bulk composition as the sample solution; in other words, different calibration curves should be constructed for samples of different composition. In evaluating the results we then often make not only interpolation along the calibration curve but also between individual calibration curves. Since calibration curves in flame photometry and in atomic absorption photometry are not always linear, the standard addition method must be used with caution [86].

In section 3.10, dealing with the errors of spectrophotometric and colorimetric determinations, we considered imperfectly monochromatic light as one of the sources of apparent deviations from the linearity of the relation between absorbance and concentration. Similarly, and perhaps to an even greater degree, this effect is manifested in atomic absorption photometry. In this case it is essential that the irradiation of the flame into which the aerosol of the analysed solution is injected, should be perfectly monochromatic, even more perfectly so than can be achieved by means of a grating or prism monochromator, and for this reason we generally use a source which offers such a radiation, e.g. a hollow cathode lamp. In emission flame photometry the monochromacity of the light incident on the detector is important only insofar as it enables us to decrease the influence of foreign elements and thus to limit the flame emission background. Therefore instruments for flame emission photometry are usually designed with filters, monochromators being used only in the more expensive ones. When, however, the highest sensitivity is needed, it is useful to limit the interfering influence of the flame background and to increase sensitivity by using a monochromator and a photomultiplier as detector.

3.13 Errors of electroanalytical determinations

Electrogravimetry is a special field of gravimetric analysis, and therefore its errors are similar to those of gravimetric analyses. Here we precipitate a metal (electrogravimetric precipitation of oxides is only of secondary importance nowadays) from the solution quantitatively, in a suitable and sufficiently pure form. Electrolytic precipitation is however generally more complete than precipitation by means of chemical reagents, and adsorption from the solution onto the metal layer is mostly quite negligible. The only difficulties which may occur in this case are an unsuitable form or loss of the metal from the electrode, and in some cases incomplete separation of two metals, and these can be eliminated by proper choice and control of the electrolysis potential and of the composition of the electrolytic solution.

Although the circumstances are more favourable for accuracy in electro-analysis than in chemical gravimetric methods, there is one less favourable circumstance which ought always to be kept in mind. The conversion factor is unity in the determination of metals precipitated in the metallic form, and thus any error of weighing will be manifested in its full magnitude in the error of the result. For this reason enough sample must be taken for analysis to make the amount of metal deposited at least 0.1 g; moreover, no unnecessarily heavy electrodes should be used. We may even consider it justifiable to weigh electrodes to five decimal places on a semi-micro-balance with a precision of $\pm$ 0.01 mg.

3.14 Errors of polarographic analyses

The polarographic method, worked out by the Nobel prize winner Professor Jaroslav Heyrovský (1890−1967) some 45 years ago, belongs today among the most frequently used physico-chemical microanalytical methods. Its applicability to the qualitative detection of depolarizers is small, owing to the inferior resolution of half-wave potentials, but it is one of the physico-chemical methods most frequently used for quantitative determinations. The concentration range which may be determined by polarographic means is very wide, $10^{-6} - 10^{-3}$ M. The most advantageous concentrations are from 5×10^{-5} to 10^{-3} M; in this concentration range the precision of the determination is independent of the absolute amount of the component determined. Moreover, with concentrations lower than 5×10^{-5} M the interfering effect of capacitative currents becomes rather large, while with concentrations greater than 10^{-3} M other interferences may again prevail.

The precision of a polarographic determination depends to a large extent on the way in which the polarographic wave is developed, and on how accurately its height can be measured. The relative error of the polarographic determination is generally in the range of $1-5\%$ [17]. Details of the reproducibility of polarographic measurements will be found in a paper by STURM [93]. In practice the most frequently employed procedure is the determination of a concentration by comparison with a standard. This may be done, in principle, by the methods described on p. 36 ff. for spectro-photometry. The standard addition method is very often used, direct comparison with a single standard by simple proportion is used less often. There are a number of disadvantages to the simple proportion method: the comparison standard solution should have an optimum concentration about the same as that of the sample, which is hard to achieve in practice, and various factors may affect the analysis of the sample, e.g. adsorption on a precipitate of the component sought, matrix effect, the pH of the solution, so that the diffusion currents for sample and standard are not really determined under the same conditions, so the results may be distorted. These influences may to a certain extent be removed by using the standard addition method, in which first the solution of unknown concentration c_1 is polarographed in a volume v_1, giving a wave with diffusion current i_{d_1}; volume v_0 of concentration c_0 is then added, giving the bigger wave i_{d_2}; we now calculate the concentration of the unknown solution from the equation

$$c_1 = \frac{i_{d_1} \cdot c_0 \cdot v_0}{i_{d_2} \cdot v_2 - i_{d_1} \cdot v_1} \tag{3.43}$$

The most advantageous conditions for carrying out this standard addition method have been described in section 2.12. The method may moreover be modified [17] by taking two equal aliquots of a sample stock solution, adding a certain amount of the standard solution to one of them, carrying out the necessary solution adjustments with both, making up to the same volume and recording polarograms for the two solutions separately. If any preliminary separation is needed, the standard is added beforehand; this decreases any possible systematic errors of the procedure.

Methods of comparison with a single standard have the disadvantage that the maximum error of the final result is given by the error of the analysis of the standard as well as of the determination proper. The calibration curve method eliminates to a great extent the variability of the results from which it is constructed, since in its construction some degree of homogenization of the data occurs. This method is specially suitable for routine analyses, offering accurate results even if the dependence of the wave-height on concentration is not strictly linear. When a given component is being determined in a solution containing other components, or if preliminary separation is needed, all other components of the sample must be added to the solutions serving in the construction of the calibration graph, or the preliminary procedure must be carried out as for the sample. It is clear, of course, that a given calibration curve holds only for samples of roughly the same composition, for a given capillary, a constant height of the mercury reservoir, equal sensitivity etc. A difference from comparison with one standard is that the temperature must be controlled to about 0.2 °C.

3.15 Errors of extraction methods

In modern chemical analysis extraction methods are frequently used to separate substances [22]. The principle of these methods is the distribution of a substance between two solvents. The practical procedure involves agitation (shaking) of the solution, usually an aqueous one, with some immiscible solvent in which the substance to be extracted is more soluble, followed by mechanical separation of the two phases. In organic and pharmaceutical analysis, extraction has been in use for a long time; in inorganic analysis, complex compounds (sometimes coloured) of different metals are extracted into solvents of lower polarity. Coloured compounds may then be measured immediately by colorimetric means, or the solvent may be evaporated after separation, and the component extracted again brought into aqueous solution and determined separately. Another possibility consists in stripping, i.e. back-extraction into an aqueous phase of a composition different (usually of a different pH) from the solution from which extraction was initially done. In trace analysis, extraction is very frequently combined with spectrography or with emission or atomic absorption photometry. The concentration of the substance in the solution decreases by extraction from the original concentration c_0 to a concentration c_1 given by

$$c_1 = c_0 \frac{v_A}{D v_B + v_A} \qquad (3.44)$$

where D is the distribution coefficient and v_A, v_B are the volumes of the phases A and B used in extraction. In the next extraction operation, the concentration of the substance extracted decreases in the original solution to

$$c_2 = c_0 \left(\frac{v_A}{D v_B + v_A} \right)^2$$

and in general, after the nth operation,

$$c_n = c_0 \left(\frac{v_A}{D v_B + v_A} \right)^n \qquad (3.45)$$

From these relations it follows, that (i) the solvent volume used should be sufficiently large, but (ii) perfect extraction will be achieved by means of repeated extraction with small solvent volumes rather than with a single extraction with a large volume, (iii) nonetheless absolutely quantitative extraction can never be achieved, so that we must be satisfied with "practically perfect" extraction, and (iv) a significant role is played by the value of the distribution coefficient D: if it is large enough, "practically complete" extraction may be achieved even with a single extraction operation; if, however, the coefficient is low, extraction must be repeated several times. This last finding is of great significance for practical analytical extraction: if the distribution coefficient D is unknown, a practical test must be done to find out the number of extractions, the solvent volume etc., needed.

Let us now calculate the relative error caused by imperfect extraction in the separation of a certain solution component. Thus, when extracting 0.20 g of iodine from 100 ml of an aqueous solution with 50 ml portions of carbon tetrachloride ($D = 85$), there remains after the first extraction $c_1 = 0.2 \left(\dfrac{100}{85 \times 50 + 100} \right) = 0.0046$ g and the relative error caused by imperfect extraction is $\varepsilon_1 = \dfrac{0.0046 \times 100}{0.2} = 2.3\%$, i.e. a substantial error. After the second extraction there remains only $c_2 = 0.2 \left(\dfrac{100}{85 \times 50 \times 100} \right)^2 = 0.0001057$ g, and the relative error is $\varepsilon_2 = \dfrac{0.0001057 \times 100}{0.2} = 0.05\%$, which is negligible. Thus in practice a double carbon tetrachloride extraction is enough to extract iodine completely from aqueous solution.

However, the situation is more complicated in the case occurring most frequently in inorganic analysis, the extraction of metal chelates. The chelate is formed by reaction of a metal ion with the reagent according to the equation

$$\text{Me}^{n+} + n\text{HX} \rightleftharpoons \text{MeX}_n + n\,\text{H}^+.$$

The dissociation constant of the chelate is $K_{\mathrm{MeX}_n} = \dfrac{[\mathrm{Me}]\,[\mathrm{HX}]^n}{[\mathrm{MeX}_n]\,[\mathrm{H}]^n}$ and the dissociation constant of the reagent $K_R = \dfrac{[\mathrm{X}]\,[\mathrm{H}]}{[\mathrm{HX}]}$. There are then two interacting processes: formation of the complex and dissociation of the reagent, i.e. processes dependent on the reagent concentration and on the hydrogen ion concentration. In addition, the solubility of the complex and of the reagent in water and in the organic solvent must be taken into account. Removal of the complex into the organic phase shifts the equilibrium of complex formation in the aqueous phase in a favourable direction, while removal of the reagent into the organic phase shifts the equilibrium of complex formation in the aqueous phase in the unfavourable direction. Therefore, instead of the distribution coefficient defined by Eq. 3.38, the so-called distribution ratio

$$g = \frac{D_{\mathrm{MeX}_n} \cdot K_{\mathrm{MeX}_n} \cdot K_R^n}{D_R^n} \cdot \left(\frac{[\mathrm{HA}]_B}{[\mathrm{H}]_A}\right)^n \tag{3.46}$$

is used, where D_{MeX_n} and D_R are the distribution coefficients of the chelate and reagent respectively, K_{MeX_n} and K_R are the dissociation constants of the chelate and reagent, $[\mathrm{HA}]_B$ is the reagent concentration in the organic phase and $[\mathrm{H}]_A$ is the hydrogen ion concentration in the aqueous phase. It is clear that extraction of the metal chelate is most quantitative when the chelate is very stable and highly soluble in the organic solvent, and when the reagent is very soluble in water and its dissociation constant is high. It is also essential to use an excess of the reagent and to regulate the pH value of the aqueous phase.

3.16 Errors of some special separation methods

Modern analytical chemistry makes use of quite a number of different separation methods. Trace analysis especially is quite unthinkable without them. These separation processes may, however, be sources of error, usually because of incompleteness of separation. One of the most important and most often used separation methods, *solvent extraction*, has just been dealt with; precipitation was discussed in section 3.8. In trace analysis, where small amounts of the element sought are to be separated in the presence of an excess of the matrix substance we could in most cases not achieve complete precipitation, and for this reason the effect of *co-precipitation* is utilized. A certain amount of a carrier is added, i.e. an element which forms insoluble compounds similar to those of the element sought, and the two elements are precipitated together. Co-precipitation is advantageous as a preliminary separation method before spectrographic determination, or for separation in activation analysis. In the latter case, the carrier added for co-precipitation of the activated element may be a non-active form of the element; after precipitation with a suitable precipitant the amount of the element present in the sample is determined by measuring the activity of the precipitate. Such determinations are not only very sensitive, they are also subject almost exclusively to random errors only.

An efficient method of separating metals is *electrolysis*. If it is to be selective, a constant electrode potential must be maintained throughout the operation. Compared with electrolysis on solid, e.g. grid electrodes, electrolysis on a mercury electrode is more suitable for separations. Elements plated out at a mercury cathode are not generally determined in this way, and this procedure is usually used for the elimination of interfering elements, e.g. Cr, Mo, Fe, Co, Ni, Cu, Ag, Zn, Cd, Ga, In, Tl, Ge, Sn, Pb, As, Bi, Se, Te and Hg. Sometimes inner electrolysis may also be used for separation purposes. A disadvantage of separational electrolysis is contamination of the solution by the anode material.

Ion-exchangers are a very efficient means of separation of quite a number of cations and anions, permitting them to be separated even from solutions diluted to such an extent that direct determination would be impossible. The application of suitable chelating agents offers many more possibilities of separation. A column of cation-exchange resin used for the separation of cations, or an anion-exchange resin used to separate anions, may be sources of a systematic error due to imperfect washing of the resin, which will occur mainly if a product of low solubility is formed. It should also be remembered, especially in routine analyses, that the capacity of the ion-exchange resin is not unlimited and should not be exceeded, as otherwise separation will be incomplete.

Distillation methods are suitable in those cases where highly volatile components of the mixture are to be separated. It is easy to distil ammonia quantitatively in the Kjeldahl process, and it has been proved that distillation is not a source of systematic error in this method. Distillation may also be used to separate AsH_3, CO_2, H_2S, SO_2, HF, SiF_4, methyl borate, and possibly some chlorides. When $AsCl_3$ (b.p. 130 °C) is distilled a high hydrochloric acid concentration (at least 25 %) must be constantly maintained, since otherwise non-volatile hydrolytic products will form; oxidation to the non-volatile arsenic(V) oxide must be avoided. These circumstances may cause low results, and it is necessary to maintain precisely the optimum experimental conditions. With other methods, where distillation need not be absolutely quantitative, or with some micromethods, the factor of the volumetric solution used to titrate the distillate may be determined with a standard carried through the entire separation procedure, so that the titre includes a correction for the incomplete character of the distillation operation. Exactly the same procedure must then be used in all the determinations.

When speaking of the errors of some modern separation processes, the majority of which are rather perfect and are generally simple to perform, we must take into consideration that their application in cases where they simplify the procedure leads to a higher precision and accuracy of the results than may be expected if the difficult classical processes are used. One more circumstance must also be considered in connection with the significance of separation processes for trace analysis. The separation of trace elements in such a "pure" manner that no contamination of the sample should occur requires a maximum of careful work. Unless this basic demand is satisfied there is no sense in considering the error aspect of separation methods when they are applied to trace analysis, since the error caused by imperfection of the separation methods will be quite negligible in comparison to the errors caused by contamination.

Chapter 4

THE APPLICATION
OF MATHEMATICAL STATISTICS

4.1 Application in assessing analytical results

Up to now we have considered errors which may occur in measurements
or in some analytical operation, discussed the errors of individual analytical
methods, investigated the influence of individual errors on the final result
and searched for conditions under which the error of measurement would
be minimum. Our considerations have always been concerned with a priori
assumptions of the possibility of occurrence of an error and of its magnitude,
but these considerations alone offered no possibility of judging the reliability
of the actual analytical results [7].

It has often been stated in discussion of criteria of the accuracy of results,
that objective criteria of accuracy and precision, of systematic or random
occurrence of errors and of values of permitted differences and similar
quantities useful in practical applications, are offered by mathematical
statistical calculations [5, 6, 7, 8, 12, 13, 23, 24, 25, 35, 42, 63, 64]. Thus
statistics are employed in a posteriori assessment of analytical results after
these have been obtained. As a matter of course, every analyst assesses
his results in his own way, but generally he will first of all consider the
agreement of parallel determinations to see whether one results differs
from the rest more than any other and then decide whether to include or
to exclude such a result, or whether more parallel determinations should
be carried out, etc. The decision is based on experience gained in the application of a given analytical method, but of course it is not quite free from some
subjective factors. Statistical tests in principle do exactly the same thing
but with the difference that they are of a more mathematical character
and that their result is quite objective and not influenced by subjective
factors.

In this chapter we shall elucidate the terms of probability calculus and
of mathematical statistics, and discuss individual cases in which statistical
methods may be applied with success. The principle will be adhered to,
that it is of more importance for the reader to learn to use these methods,
than to master their theoretical basis.

4.2 Probability

The term probability will be encountered very often in mathematical statistics, and therefore must be first briefly explained.

When a given phenomenon is repeated and only some of the total number of events are favourable, we use the term mathematical probability P to denote the ratio between the number of favourable events m and the number of all possible events n

$$P = \frac{m}{n} \qquad (4.1)$$

Probability may attain values from zero to unity: if $m = n$, i.e. if all possible events are favourable ones, $P = 1$ and we speak of certainty, the probability of an unfavourable case being $P = 0$. The greater the value of P, the greater of course the probability that the favourable event will take place. Probability may sometimes be expressed in per cent, i.e.

$$P = \frac{100 \cdot m}{n} \% \qquad (4.2)$$

Besides this *"classic" definition of probability*, which is applicable only where it is possible to determine a given number of possible and favourable events, and where the number of possible events is finite, the so-called *statistical definition of probability* is also used. According to this definition, probability is the ratio between the number of occurrences of the event A in relation to all observations, experiments, measurements, etc., carried out, i.e.

$$p = \frac{n_A}{n_0} \qquad (4.3)$$

This definition can also be used for $n = \infty$ because it does not necessitate the exhaustion of all possibilities, although it is demanded that the number of observations n_0 be large enough. Evidently the probability p determined according to this statistical definition need not always lead to an absolutely accurate value of the true probability in terms of the classic definition. However, this is not required; it suffices for $p = n_A/n_0$ to approach the value of P in the limit for $n_0 \rightarrow \infty$ or $n_0 \rightarrow n$.

Let us illustrate the rules which hold for some simple cases of probability, by means of an example with playing cards. Let us for example calculate the probability of selecting an ace out of 52 bridge cards. The deck of cards includes four aces, i.e. $m = 4$ and $n = 52$, which means that $P = \frac{4}{52} = 0.077$, i.e. $P = 7.7\%$. Let us formulate the example in a different way: what is the probability of selecting either the ace of spades, or the ace of hearts etc? The probability of choosing the ace of spades is $P_s = \frac{1}{52} = 0.019$, of choosing the ace of hearts, $P_h = \frac{1}{52} = 0.019$ etc. Evidently the probabilities must be added to give $P_s + P_h + P_e + P_d = \frac{4}{52}$. Hence follows the general rule: if the events A, B, C may occur, A and C being for example favourable ones, the probability that either the event A or the event C will occur is equal to the sum of the individual probabilities, $P = P_A + P_C$. It is quite logical that $P > P_A$ or P_C, since the condition "either—or" means actually that the number of favourable events is increased. The situation is quite different when we want to find the probability that we shall select—without returning the cards selected—two aces in consecutive selections. The probability of selecting the first ace is $P_1 = 4/52$ and of selecting the other, $P_2 = 3/51$, because the second time the deck we are selecting from has only 51 cards, including only three aces. Here of course the conditions are much less favourable than with a single selection, because if an ace is selected the first time, another ace need not necessarily be selected the second time. The probability of occurrence of the events A *and* C is given by the product of the individual probabilities: $P = P_A \cdot P_C$, i.e. in our case $P = \dfrac{4}{52} \cdot \dfrac{3}{51} =$

$= \dfrac{12}{2652} = 0.0045$. The example of bridge cards may also be used to show the manifestation of the "statistical" character of the probability thus calculated. Since the probability of selecting any ace whatever is $P = 4/52 = 1/13$, if a series of thirteen consecutive selections were carried out, the card selected being put back each time, it might be expected that in one of the thirteen selections an ace would be found. In reality, however, it might happen that in one such series no ace would be found at all, while in another series two aces would appear, etc. In a large number of selections, however, e.g. 13 000, the number of cases in which an ace was selected would certainly approach 1 000; in other words the statistical probability should, in the limit, approach the probability P.

Of course many more rules apply to probability calculations. Those mentioned above will, however, suffice for the following discussion.

4.3 Positive and negative deviations from accurate results; the binomial distribution

When a number of parallel determinations of a sample (with μ the true content of the component determined) are carried out by means of a method which is subject to no systematic error, the results $x_1, x_2, x_3, ..., x_n$, in general x_i, are obtained; some of these will be greater than μ and some will be smaller. The value of the deviation d of the result from the true value

$$d = \mu - x_i \qquad (4.4)$$

will be positive for $\mu > x_i$ and negative for $x_i > \mu$. Let us now classify the individual deviations by signs only, irrespective of their magnitude, noting the possible cases which may occur for a given number of determinations n.

When *only one determination* is carried out, i.e. $n = 1$, there are only two possibilities: either the deviation is positive, or it is negative. Diagrammatically the result may be set down as

$n = 1$

$$+ \qquad -$$

$$P_+ = \left(\frac{1}{2}\right) \qquad P_- = \left(\frac{1}{2}\right)$$

The overall probability, i.e. the probability of either a positive or a negative deviation is $P_1 = P_+ + P_- = \left(\dfrac{1}{2}\right) + \left(\dfrac{1}{2}\right) = 1$.

When *two determinations* are carried out, $n = 2$, and there are three cases possible: both results $+$, both $-$, or one $+$ and one $-$, or the reverse. Diagrammatically:

$n = 2$

$$++ \qquad\qquad \begin{array}{c} +\,- \\ -\,+ \end{array} \qquad\qquad -\,-$$

$$P_{2+} = \left(\frac{1}{4}\right) \qquad P_{+-} = \left(\frac{1}{2}\right) \qquad P_{2-} = \left(\frac{1}{4}\right)$$

The overall possibility is

$$P_2 = \left(\frac{1}{4}\right) + \left(\frac{1}{2}\right) + \left(\frac{1}{4}\right)$$

Expressing this in such a way that every partial probability is expressed in powers of 1/2, we obtain for P_2

$$P_2 = \left(\frac{1}{2}\right)^2 + 2\left(\frac{1}{2}\right)\cdot\left(\frac{1}{2}\right) + \left(\frac{1}{2}\right)^2 = 1$$

For *three determinations*, $n = 3$, the probability is expressed diagrammatically as

$n = 3$

$$+++ \qquad \begin{array}{c} ++\,- \\ +\,-+ \\ -++ \end{array} \qquad \begin{array}{c} --+ \\ -+- \\ +-- \end{array} \qquad ----$$

$$P_{3+} = \left(\frac{1}{8}\right); \quad P_{2+1-} = \left(\frac{3}{8}\right); \quad P_{1+2-} = \left(\frac{3}{8}\right); \quad P_{3-} = \left(\frac{1}{8}\right)$$

The overall probability is

$$P_3 = \left(\frac{1}{8}\right) + \left(\frac{3}{8}\right) + \left(\frac{3}{8}\right) + \left(\frac{1}{8}\right)$$

or, expressed in a different way,

$$P_3 = \left(\frac{1}{2}\right)^3 + 3\left(\frac{1}{2}\right)^2\cdot\left(\frac{1}{2}\right) + 3\left(\frac{1}{2}\right)\left(\frac{1}{2}\right)^2 + \left(\frac{1}{2}\right)^3 = 1$$

In this way we may proceed to higher values of n.

Instead, let us mention the expression for the overall probability P_n, which of course must always be equal to unity. Quite generally it may be written as the binomial

$$P_n = \left(\frac{1}{2} + \frac{1}{2}\right)^n$$

$$P_n = \binom{n}{0}\left(\frac{1}{2}\right)^n + \binom{n}{1}\left(\frac{1}{2}\right)^{n-1}\left(\frac{1}{2}\right) + \binom{n}{2}\left(\frac{1}{2}\right)^{n-2}\left(\frac{1}{2}\right)^2 + \ldots +$$

$$+ \binom{n}{n-1}\left(\frac{1}{2}\right)\left(\frac{1}{2}\right)^{n-1} + \binom{n}{n}\left(\frac{1}{2}\right)^n = 1$$

or

$$P_n = \Sigma \binom{n}{k}\left(\frac{1}{2}\right)^{n-k}\left(\frac{1}{2}\right)^k = 1 \qquad\qquad (4.5)$$

where the (n/k) values for $k \leq n$ (k and n being positive integers), are the combinatorial coefficients (binomial coefficients) of the Pascal triangle (see Table 4.1). The factors 1/2 always occur here because the probability of the result x_i being greater than μ is equal to the probability of the result x_i being smaller than μ: in both cases this probability is equal to 1/2. To facilitate the calculations, Table 4.2 gives the values of $(1/2)^n$ for various values of n. The rule of equal probability of occurrence of two events need not always hold, and therefore the *binomial distribution* [4] is written quite generally as

$$P_n = (p + q)^n \tag{4.6}$$

where the probability of occurrence of the individual events is $p + q = 1$.

Table 4.1 The Pascal Triangle: According to the Binomial Theorem, the Binomial Coefficients may be Determined from the Pascal Triangle

$$\binom{0}{0} \qquad\qquad 1$$

$$\binom{1}{0} \quad \binom{1}{1} \qquad\qquad 1 \quad 1$$

$$\binom{2}{0} \quad \binom{2}{1} \quad \binom{2}{2} \qquad\qquad 1 \quad 2 \quad 1$$

$$\binom{3}{0} \quad \binom{3}{1} \quad \binom{3}{2} \quad \binom{3}{3} \qquad 1 \quad 3 \quad 3 \quad 1$$

$$\binom{4}{0} \quad \binom{4}{1} \quad \binom{4}{2} \quad \binom{4}{3} \quad \binom{4}{4} \quad 1 \quad 4 \quad 6 \quad 4 \quad 1$$

Note: $\binom{n}{k} = \dfrac{n!}{k!(n-k)!}$ and $\binom{n}{k} = \binom{n-1}{k-1} + \binom{n-1}{k}$

$n! = 1 \times 2 \times 3 \ldots (n-1) \times n$

$\binom{n}{0} = \binom{n}{n} = 1$

Table 4.2. Values of $(1/2)^n$ for Calculations of the Probability of the Maximum Error from the Binomial Distribution

n	$\left(\dfrac{1}{2}\right)^n$
0	1
1	0.5
2	0.25
3	0.125
4	0.0625
5	0.03125
6	0.015625
7	0.0078125
8	0.00390625
9	0.001953125
10	0.0009765625

We shall now be concerned with determining the most probable number of occurrences of an event having probability p: it may be proved mathematically that this expected value E is given by

$$E = n \cdot p. \tag{4.7}$$

For example, for 20 analyses the number of results larger than μ may be expected to be $E = \dfrac{1}{2} \times 20 = 10$; for 21 analyses we find $E = \dfrac{1}{2} \times 21 = 10.5$; this means that there is an equal probability of there being 10 or 11 results larger than μ. The binomial distribution may also be used in a different way; it has been shown in section 1.5 that the maximum relative error of the function $y = f(x_1, x_2, \ldots, x_n)$ is equal to the sum of the relative errors $\varepsilon_y = \varepsilon_{x_1} + \varepsilon_{x_2} + \ldots + \varepsilon_{x_n}$ but that the actual error achieves this magnitude only in exceptional cases. The binomial distribution may be used to calculate the probability of all errors of measurement having the same sign, and thus being additive. This probability is given by the expression

$$P_{max} = 2 \cdot \left(\frac{1}{2}\right)^n = \left(\frac{1}{2}\right)^{n-1} \tag{4.8}$$

With an increasing number of measurements (n) from which the final result is calculated, the probability of all errors being additive decreases rapidly. Thus for $n = 2$, $P_{max} = 0.5$; for $n = 3$, $P_{max} = 0.25$ and for $n = 6$, P_{max} is only 0.031, in other words it is probable that the errors of all six measurements will have the same sign in only three cases out of one hundred; in all other cases positive as well as negative errors will occur, and they will compensate each other at least in part. The possibilities of further calculations with the use of the binomial distribution are described by ECKSCHLAGER [57].

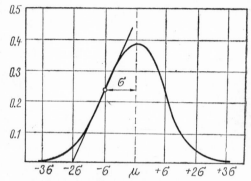

FIG. 4.1. The Gaussian curve. For $\mu = 0$ the value of the standard deviation σ is given by the abscissa of the point of inflexion. The tangent of the curve at the point of inflexion intersects the x axis at the point 2σ.

4.4 The Gaussian distribution; the normal distribution of random errors

We have seen in the preceding section that the probability of occurrence of results greater than the true value μ is always equal to the probability of smaller results. Let us now investigate the magnitude of deviations from the true value; the analyst is always interested not only in whether his results are higher or lower, but also in how much they differ from the true value.

Expressing the probability of occurrence of the results x_i in the form of a frequency, we are able to express the dependence of the frequency of this quantity x_i on its difference from μ by the theoretical function

$$f(x_i) = \frac{1}{\sigma \sqrt{2\pi}} \cdot \exp\left[-\frac{1}{2}\left(\frac{x_i - \mu}{\sigma}\right)^2\right] \tag{4.9}$$

where besides the constants π and the base of natural logarithms, we have two parameters, *the true (expected) value* μ and the *standard deviation* σ, which we are going to discuss in detail later. The distribution of values that is governed by this mathematical model is called the Gaussian or normal distribution. The graphic illustration of such a distribution is the Gaussian curve (Fig. 4.1). There are some specific properties of this distribution. The value of $x_i = \mu$ has the highest frequency of occurrence; the more x_i differs from μ, the lower its frequency. The curve is symmetrical, i.e. not only is the number of all positive deviations equal to the number of all negative deviations, but also the numbers of positive and negative deviations of a certain magnitude, irrespective of the sign, are equal. The symmetrical character of the results is a very important property, as we shall see later. Thus the curve has a maximum at $x_i = \mu$, and two inflexion points at $x_i = \mu \pm \sigma$ (which follows from the properties of inflexion in differential calculus), and the two sides approach the abscissa asymptotically. It should be added, rather as a matter of interest, that the Gaussian distribution is a limiting case of the binomial distribution for $n \to \infty$ [4, 14]. We have seen already in section 1.2 that the origin of random errors is explained by the addition and compensation of immeasurably small so-called elementary errors. The Gaussian distribution has been derived theoretically on the assumption that every value x_i is influenced by an infinite number of infinitesimally small elementary errors, which may equally probably be positive or negative. Thus the Gaussian distribution represents the most common mathematical model of the distribution of analytical results, subject to random errors only. Most deviations from the Gaussian distribution occur because these basic assumptions have not been fulfilled, and this will be discussed in section 4.12. The function which expresses the normal distribution of results subject only to random errors, is a continuous function and holds for values from $-\infty$ to $+\infty$. The real distribution of analytical results will, of course, never fulfil these conditions; observed values can never be $\pm\infty$. Moreover, their distribution is never quite continuous, because they originate from calculations based on values read on a scale, which naturally is always discontinuous. Thus the Gaussian or normal distribution is, in fact, a limiting law of the distribution of results which are subject to random errors, and expresses the real distribution of such results only in the vicinity of μ, e.g. in the interval $\mu \pm 3\sigma$.

4.5 Parameters of the normal distribution of errors

Equation 4.9 involves two parameters: the mean expected value μ and the scatter σ^2. For illustration, let us demonstrate the influence of the two parameters on the shape and position of Gaussian curves in a co-ordinate system, using the examples of Figs. 4.2 a and b.

Figure 4.2a shows two Gaussian curves with different values of μ (μ_1, μ_2), but with the same standard deviation σ. The shape of the two curves is the same (by shifting the second curve by a distance $\mu_2 - \mu_1$ the two curves can be made to cover each other), but their position with respect to the origin of the co-ordinate system differs. Figure 4.2a in fact illustrates the distribution of results of a large number of parallel analyses, by the same method, of two similar samples containing amounts μ_1 and μ_2 of the component determined. Figure 4.2b shows two Gaussian curves with the same value of μ, but with different σ values; their position in the co-ordinate system is the same but their shape is different. The curve having the lower value σ_1 is rather narrow and high, there being a higher frequency of values close to μ than in the case of the second flatter curve with greater σ_2. In practice, Fig. 4.2b illustrates the distribution of the results of a large number of parallel analyses of one sample, carried out by means of two accurate methods, giving, however, results of differing precision, i.e. methods of different reproducibilities.

Thus the parameter μ, or rather its difference from the true value is a measure of the accuracy of the method, while the parameter σ serves as a measure of precision (reproducibility). Hence also follows the significance of the Gaussian distribution of random errors in the assessment of analytical methods [8, 35].

Mathematical statistics, especially calculations based on the Gaussian law, are used for a posteriori calculations of results obtained in the analysis of a given sample by a given analytical method, e.g. for comparison with results obtained by means of a different method, with a different sample, etc.

The calculation of the values of normal error distribution parameters is a problem of immense practical significance; it will be discussed in the following two sections.

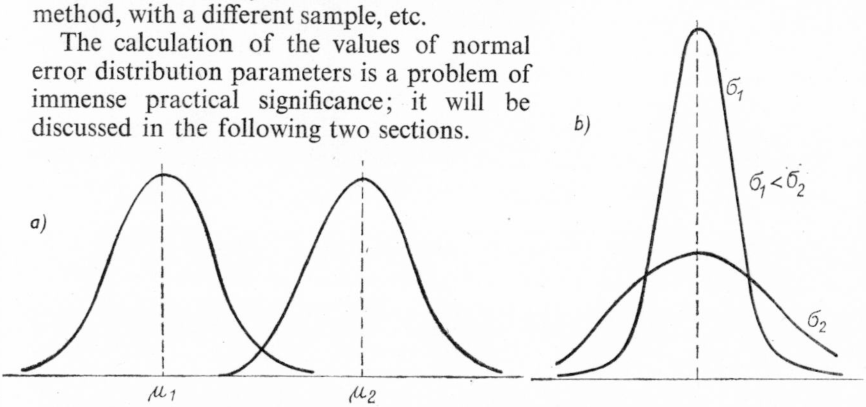

FIG. 4.2. Influence of the parameters on the shape and position of the Gaussian curve
(a) Equal values of σ, different values of μ; identical curves, separated by a distance $\mu_2 - \mu_1$. (b) equal values of μ, different values of σ; the peaks of the curves lie at the same value, but their width differs

4.6 Estimate of the mean value

The normal (Gaussian) distribution law has been derived for an infinite population, and therefore it should hold exactly only for an infinite number of results of parallel determinations. In analytical practice, however, excessively large numbers of determinations are never made, rather the reverse being usually the case; the difficulty of performance and the duration of the entire analytical procedure makes it impractical to carry out more than two, or occasionally three, parallel analyses of the same sample, a difference from physical measurements which can easily be repeated many times. It is therefore never possible to determine precisely the value of the error distribution parameters, and they can only be estimated. In the sense of mathematical statistics, an estimate is the value of a parameter exactly calculated by means of a given relationship from values obtained by precise measurement. The resulting value, of course, is not a precise value of the parameter, it is only an "estimate" because it has been calculated from a limited, finite number of results, n. In calculations we must therefore differentiate strictly between the actual parameter and its estimated value, the estimate having some specific properties relative to the actual parameter value [4, 14].

Every estimate has a certain distribution. The calculated estimate value may differ in individual cases from the assumed parameter, but in the limit for $n \to \infty$ it must asymptotically approach the true value of the parameter estimated, i.e. it must be *consistent*. As long as the value of the estimate is not equal to that of the parameter, it should be symmetrically distributed about the parameter value, i.e. the estimate value should be *unbiased* and not, for example, negatively biased (it would underestimate the parameter value) or positively biased (overestimation). At the same time, it should have the important property of being *efficient*, i.e. the scatter of the estimate around the true parameter should be as small as possible. Since scatter around a given value can be assessed numerically, the efficiency of individual estimates can be compared by the relative efficiency method, i.e. the ratio of scatter values of the two estimates. In statistical estimates the concern is most often with asymptotically efficient estimates, i.e. estimates which are efficient only for $n \to \infty$. Frequently a given parameter may be estimated in different ways, the individual estimates usually leading to values which differ mutually to some extent and have different properties. The method of calculation should then be selected according to the properties required of the estimate.

The true parameters of a probability distribution are usually unknown. They are the parameters of the basic population of data, which is usually infinite in scope and the existence of which is frequently admitted only hypothetically. These parameters are approximated by means of estimates from observed populations, which in this respect are considered to be "random selections" of the hypothetical basic population [4].

It can be proved mathematically, that a consistent, unbiased and very efficient estimate of the parameter μ of the Gaussian distribution is the arithmetic mean

$$\bar{x} = \frac{1}{n} \Sigma x_i \qquad (4.10)$$

Table 4.3.

Efficiency of the Median Relative to the Arithmetic Mean

n	Efficiency
2	1.00
3	0.74
4	0.84
5	0.70
6	0.78
7	0.68
8	0.74
9	0.67
10	0.72
∞	0.64

The distribution of the selected mean of the basic normal population is also normal. The mean represents the most probable value of the parameter μ, but for small values of n it is sensitive to the symmetry of the distribution, i.e. the extreme values, which can be subject to gross error. In order to eliminate the influence of the extreme values, the median $\tilde{x}$ is sometimes used as an estimate of the parameter μ: the median represents a value which divides in half the set of values put in order of magnitude; with sets of uneven numbers of members (an uneven number of values) the middle value is taken as median, and if the number of members is even, the mean of the two middle values is used. Thus for a set of two values $x_1 < x_2$, the median is $\tilde{x} = {}^1/_2(x_1 + x_2)$; for a set of three values $x_1 < x_2 < x_3$ the median $\tilde{x} = x_2$ and for the set $x_1 < x_2 < x_3 < x_4$ the median is $\tilde{x} = {}^1/_2(x_2 + x_3)$. The median is independent of the extreme values, because for $n \geq 3$ the extreme values are not included in the calculation at all, but it is a less efficient estimate than the mean. The relative efficiency of the median compared with the arithmetic mean is given in Table 4.3.

From this table it follows that the median is a more efficient estimate for an even than odd number of results, and that its efficiency decreases at first rather rapidly with increasing value of n, but later decreases only slowly. With increasing n the difference between the efficiency of the the median for even and odd numbers of analyses also decreases.

In practical analytical chemistry the mean (sometimes the geometric mean, as will be shown later) is used nearly exclusively as an estimate of the parameter μ. Sometimes use is made of the circumstance that the median value is not at all influenced by random gross errors. For a symmetrical distribution (and thus also for the normal distribution) and an infinite number of results, the equation $\bar{x} = \tilde{x}$ should be valid. For small values of n this cannot of course be assumed, but nevertheless the difference $x - \tilde{x}$ should not be too large. A large difference between the two would mean that the set of data obtained does not have a very symmetrical distribution, and that therefore one of the extreme values may be subject to gross error.

In a determination of zinc in a standard sample containing 10.01% Zn, chelatometric titration resulted in values of 9.98%, 10.02%, 10.04% and 10.46% Zn. The mean is 10.125% Zn and the median is 10.03% Zn. In this case the median is the more accurate value. The difference between median and average is rather great, 0.095%. After the last value, where there was suspicion of over-titration, had been excluded and another analysis carried out, 10.03% Zn was found. Now the average is 10.017% Zn and the median 10.025% Zn, the difference between mean and median being only 0.008%. Both estimates, mean as well as median, agree quite well with the true value (both are a little high), but the efficiency of the median is, according to Table 4.3, only 0.84 with respect to the average.

Let us mention one more, mathematically indefinable, property of estimates. Parameter estimates represent a certain "condensation" of information inherent in the results of measurement. When all values of results obtained are utilized in the estimate of a given parameter, full use is made of all information which concerns a given property of the values measured and is contained in the results. When, however, only a part of the results is used for the estimate, we are losing the information contained in those results which are not included in the calculation. For example in calculation of the mean of seven results of parallel analyses, all the values obtained will be utilized according to Eq. 4.10 and each of these values will participate in the final calculation of the estimate. When, however, the median is calculated from these results, i.e. in this case $\tilde{x} = x_4$, the numerical quantitative value of only one result will be involved, while the role of the other six results consists only in determining the value of x_4 as the median value of the set. Thus their role is the same as if their numerical value were unknown and we knew only that they lie in the series $x_1, x_2, x_3 < x_4 < < x_5, x_6, x_7$. It is clear that in this case we are losing a substantial part of the information contained in our results. The greater the value of n, the greater is this loss of information in the calculation of the median.

4.7 The estimate of the standard deviation

Scatter, σ^2, is the second important parameter of the Gaussian distribution. It is often called the *variance*. This parameter, or rather its estimate, is mainly used in scatter (or variance) analysis, which will be described briefly in one of the following sections. The square root of scatter, *the standard deviation*, is far more important in practice. The standard deviation represents the absolute error for that value of x_1 for which the Gaussian error distribution curve has a point of inflexion. It has already been mentioned that the value of the standard deviation σ is a measure of reproducibility; the smaller the value of σ, the more are the results accumulated around the true value and the more precise they are. The value of s_0, defined by Eq. 4.11 is an unbiased and efficient estimate of the parameter σ.

$$s_0 = \sqrt{\frac{1}{n} \cdot \Sigma d_i^2} = \sqrt{\frac{1}{n} \Sigma (\mu - x_i)^2} \qquad (4.11)$$

In practice, of course, the value of μ, and therefore also of the absolute error d_i, is unknown. However, replacing the absolute error with the deviation Δ, we obtain the estimate

$$s_1 = \sqrt{\frac{1}{n} \Sigma \Delta^2} = \sqrt{\frac{1}{n} \Sigma (\bar{x} - x_i)^2} \qquad (4.12)$$

which is consistent, but not unbiased. The reason is the following: the sum of squares of deviations from the mean value is a minimum sum of squares — in fact, it has been defined thus as the value for which the sum of squares of deviations is minimum — and therefore it is, in general, smaller than Σd_i^2, so that the expression s_1 as an estimate of the parameter σ of the basic set will underestimate the parameter in question. This estimate is sometimes used in those cases where the concern is not with estimating the parameter σ of the basic set, i.e. the standard deviation as a "constant" of a given analytical method, but instead with an estimate of the degree of scatter of individual results around the mean of a series of parallel determinations carried out with one sample. In agreement with all this the value of s_1 will be used later as a criterion of scatter in the determination of the presence of a gross error in one of a series of parallel analyses. The parameter σ of the basic set, i.e. the standard deviation s of a given analytical method, is always estimated from the relationship

$$s = \sqrt{\frac{1}{n-1} \Sigma \Delta^2} = \sqrt{\frac{1}{n-1} \Sigma (x - x_i)^2} \qquad (4.13)$$

This estimate is consistent and unbiased, but not efficient. It is only asymptotically efficient, i.e. efficient for $n \to \infty$. It can be shown that this is the most efficient of all unbiased estimates of the parameter σ which are independent of μ.

The expression $(n - 1)$ in the denominator of Eq. 4.13 can be justified theoretically [4]. It represents the *number of degree of freedom*, usually denoted by v, and given by the number of independent results. Because the mean value x, which occurs in Eq. 4.13, depends on the values of x_i

(therefore differing from μ in Eq. 4.11), one of the n determinations is not independent of $\bar{x}$ and the others. The concept of degrees of freedom will be encountered several times in the following sections. The numerical calculation of the expression $\Sigma(x - x_i)^2$ from Eqs. 4.12 and 4.13 is rather difficult; the differences of all results from the mean must be determined, and the squares of these differences computed, each separately. Moreover, the mean value must frequently be rounded off to the same number of digits with which the values of x_i are determined, which again cannot leave the value of s uninfluenced. Therefore, in practical calculations, the sum of squares of deviations is replaced by the expression

$$\Sigma(\bar{x} - x_i)^2 = \Sigma x_i^2 - \frac{1}{n}(\Sigma x_i)^2 = \Sigma x_i^2 - n\bar{x}^2 \qquad (4.14)$$

with which the calculation can be done easily with the use of a desk calculating machine, and the error of rounding off the mean value will not influence the result.

The estimate according to Eq. 4.13 is efficient only asymptotically, which means that in order to obtain a reliable value for the estimate of the parameter σ of the basic set, a large number, at least 15 to 20, of parallel determinations must be carried out with one perfectly homogeneous sample. There is nothing to justify the view that the difficulties connected with such a large "verification series" of parallel analyses are the greatest hindrance to the application in practical analytical chemistry of parametric methods of mathematical statistics, based on the standard deviation.

Let us try to obtain reliable estimates of σ by means of two methods usable in practical analysis. For the first method, a large number of determinations is needed, but these should be carried out with different samples, a process which is carried out anyway in an analytical laboratory; the second method does not require a large number of determinations; on the contrary, it demands a small number of parallel determinations.

The first method, perhaps the best for an evaluation of the reproducibility of an analytical method, is an estimate of the σ value from the results of n parallel determinations carried out with m samples. If a laboratory systematically carries out analytical control of a product or a raw material, sufficient results are available for statistical treatment. A condition of the use of this method is that analyses must be performed under roughly the same conditions and with an approximately constant composition of the samples [42, 48]. If the content of the component determined in the samples varies too much, the method requires further modification [48].

Let us therefore assume that we are carrying out n parallel determinations and have analysed m samples. The results of the analysis of a given sample are now arranged in order of magnitude and written down in a table for the individual samples (see page 88). (see page 88)
The estimate of the standard deviation, s_s, is now calculated from

$$s_s = \sqrt{\frac{1}{m(n-1)} \cdot \sum_{j=1}^{m} \sum_{i=1}^{n} (x_{ji} - \bar{x}_j)^2}. \qquad (4.15)$$

In practice, the expression below the square root is computed by calculating, separately, for each sample, deviations from the mean, squaring and adding;

Sample	Results	Mean value
1	$x_{1,1};\ x_{1,2};\ \dots;\ x_{1,n}$	$\bar{x}_1$
2	$x_{2,1};\ x_{2,2};\ \dots;\ x_{2,n}$	$\bar{x}_2$
$\vdots$	$\vdots$	$\vdots$
m	$x_{m,1};\ x_{m,2};\ \dots;\ x_{m,n}$	$\bar{x}_m$
		$x = \dfrac{1}{m} \displaystyle\sum_{j=1}^{m} \bar{x}_j$

this is repeated with the next sample and all the sums of squares of deviations are added. The numerical calculation according to this equation is not easy, but in special cases only pairs of determinations ($n = 2$) are done:

Sample	Results	Difference of the greatest and smallest results	Square of the difference
1	$x_{1,1};\ x_{1,2}$	$R_1 = x_{1,1} - x_{1,2}$	R_1^2
2	$x_{2,1};\ x_{2,2}$	$R_2 = x_{2,1} - x_{2,2}$	R_2^2
$\vdots$	$\vdots$	$\vdots$	$\vdots$
m	$x_{m,1};\ x_{m,2}$	$R_m = x_{m,1} - x_{m,2}$	R_m^2
			$\displaystyle\sum_{j=1}^{m} R_j^2$

The expression for the standard deviation s_s is then simplified to

$$s_s = \sqrt{\frac{1}{2m} \cdot \sum_{j=1}^{m} R_j^2} \tag{4.16}$$

where R_j is called the range. The range, i.e. the difference between the greatest and smallest value obtained, has a mathematically definable distribution, which depends on the standard deviation of the results, i.e. on the parameter σ of the basic set.

This brings us to the second method of estimating the standard deviation from results which are usually available in analytical laboratories. It may be proved that

$$s_R = k_n \cdot R \tag{4.17}$$

where k_n is a constant which is given for different values of n in Table 4.4, and s_R is a constant biased estimate of the parameter σ. Table 4.4 also gives the relative efficiency of this estimate as compared with the estimate of the value as obtained by use of Eq. 4.13. The "efficiency" mentioned here is not actually efficiency in the sense of the mathematical definition, because the estimate according to Eq. 4.13 is efficient only asymptotically. Evidently this estimate of the standard deviation is the most advantageous, especially for the smallest numbers of parallel determinations (for low values of n it is the most efficient) and it should not be used for values of $n > 10$.

For routine analytical practice it is moreover immensely advantageous in its great simplicity: it suffices to multiply the range, i.e. the difference between the greatest and smallest analytical result, by a constant which is found in tables for a given number of results n. The use of this estimate in practical analysis has been recommended by DEAN and DIXON [46]. It is, in fact, the only method of estimating σ from a small number of parallel determinations, and it is suitable not only as a measure of precision of the results of a given analysis, performed under a definite set of conditions and with a given sample, but also as an estimate of the standard deviation of a given

Table 4.4. Values of Coefficient k_n for Estimating the Standard Deviation from the Range, and the Efficiency of this Estimate [46]

n	k_n	Efficiency
2	0.8862	1.00
3	0.5908	0.99
4	0.4857	0.98
5	0.4299	0.96
6	0.3946	0.93
7	0.3698	0.91
8	0.3512	0.89
9	0.3367	0.87
10	0.3249	0.85

analytical method, if the following procedure is employed: a large number m of analyses is performed in such a manner that n parallel determinations are carried out with each sample; the value of R_j is calculated for each sample in a similar way to the calculation given in the scheme on p. 88; however, n must be the same for all samples in this case, although it need not be 2; any value is suitable as long as it is not too large. From these values

we then compute $\overline{R} = \dfrac{1}{m} \Sigma R_j$, i.e. the mean range, and we substitute

the mean range in Eq. 4.17, multiplying it finally with the value of k_n from Table 4.4 for the given value of n.

When the range is used for any calculation whatsoever, some circumstances must be kept in mind. First of all, the estimate of the standard deviation from the range by use of the k_n value has been derived on the assumption the Gaussian law applies. It may be shown, however, that if this method is utilized for a calculation of the standard deviation of results, the distribution of which is symmetrical but not exactly normal (e.g. a slightly flatter or narrower distribution), no great error is committed. This, of course, does not hold for results the distribution of which is not symmetrical. Moreover it is evident that some information is lost in this process, since for $n > 2$ the range is calculated from the two extreme results only, not from all results, and these extreme values are the most prone to gross errors. Another important but not unfavourable circumstance is the fact that the estimate s_R has a probability distribution differing from that of the estimates s_0 or s. It is therefore impossible to substitute the estimate s_R for the estimate s in all relationships, as some of them have to be modified for the use of s_R. This will be discussed later, e.g. in section 4.15.

While discussing the estimates of the parameter σ, which characterizes the distribution of results around the mean value, let us also mention the mean deviation from the median

$$d_m = \frac{\Sigma \, | \, x_i - \tilde{x} \, |}{n} \tag{4.18}$$

This scatter characteristic, defined as the mean of the absolute values of deviations from the median, can be determined numerically very easily according to the equation

$$d_m = \frac{1}{n} \, [\Sigma (x_i > \tilde{x}) - \Sigma (x_i < \tilde{x})]$$

omitting the median value itself if n is odd.

All scatter characteristics mentioned here, i.e. standard deviation, range, estimate of the standard deviation by means of the range, and finally the mean deviation from the median, are in fact also a measure of the precision of analytical results. In principle they characterize the absolute precision of results of analyses. If we need data for relative precision, they may also be used to calculate relative values, e.g. the coefficient of variation (or relative standard deviation) v:

$$v = \frac{s}{x} = \frac{s}{x} \cdot 100 \% \tag{4.19}$$

This characteristic has the property that it becomes the smaller, the more precise the results are. For this reason KAISER and SPECKER [71] have introduced the quantity

$$\Gamma = \frac{1}{v} = \frac{x}{s} \tag{4.20}$$

which increases with rising precision.

4.8 The standard deviation of the mean value

The arithmetic means represents, as we have seen in section 4.6, the best estimate of the final result of parallel determinations. Its scatter is characterized by the standard deviation of the mean

$$\sigma_{\bar{x}} = \frac{1}{\sqrt{n}} \cdot \sigma \tag{4.21}$$

where n is the number of determinations from which the mean value has been obtained. If a large series of parallel determinations is involved, the standard deviation of the mean is calculated according to the relation

$$s_{\bar{x}} = \sqrt{\frac{1}{n(n-1)} \Sigma (\bar{x} - x_i)^2} \tag{4.22}$$

while if a number n of parallel determinations carried out with m different samples is being used, the formula employed is

$$s_{\bar{x}} = \sqrt{\frac{1}{mn(n-1)} \Sigma (\bar{x}_j - x_{ij})^2} \tag{4.23}$$

It may be shown that the mean has a normal distribution with scatter σ^2/n; this is corroborated by the Eqs. 4.22 and 4.23 which are consistent and asymptotically efficient estimates. The standard deviation of the mean, $s_{\bar{x}}$, can be determined with the use of the range by means of the formula

$$s_{\bar{x}} = \frac{k_n}{\sqrt{n}} \cdot R \qquad (4.24)$$

The distribution of this estimate naturally differs from those of the two preceding estimates, and it can only be used for results the distribution of which is normal or at least symmetrical. To facilitate the calculation of the standard deviation of the mean value, table 4.5 gives values of $\sqrt{n}$, $1/\sqrt{n}$, $k_n/\sqrt{n}$ and $n(n-1)$ for different values of n.

Table 4.5. Values of $\sqrt{n}$, $1/\sqrt{n}$, $k_n/\sqrt{n}$ and $n(n-1)$
for Different Numbers of Determinations, n

n	$\sqrt{n}$	$\dfrac{1}{\sqrt{n}}$	$\dfrac{k_n}{\sqrt{n}}$	$n(n-1)$
2	1.4142	0.7071	0.6266	2
3	1.7321	0.5373	0.3411	6
4	2.0000	0.5000	0.2428	12
5	2.2361	0.4472	0.1922	20
6	2.4495	0.4082	0.1611	30
7	2.6458	0.3780	0.1398	42
8	2.8284	0.3535	0.1241	56
9	3.0000	0.3333	0.1122	72
10	3.1623	0.3162	0.1027	90

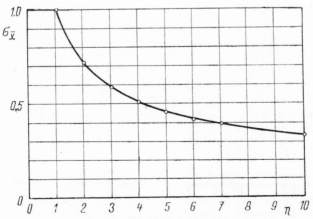

FIG. 4.3. Connection of $\sigma_{\bar{x}}$ with n.

From Eqs. 4.21 − 4.24 it follows that the estimate of the parameter μ by means of the arithmetic mean $\bar{x}$ is always a better estimate than the results

of an individual determination, and it is the better, (i) the better is the reproducibility of the individual determinations, and (ii) the greater the number
of determinations n from which the mean has been calculated. From Fig. 4.3,
illustrating the dependence of the value of $\sigma_{\bar{x}}$ on the value of n, it follows
that with a small number of determinations every extra result means a substantial improvement of the precision of the mean value, while with a larger
number of determinations the carrying out of more analyses does not have
a substantial influence on the final precision of the mean. It will be shown
later that this property of the standard deviation of the mean may be
utilized for the determination of a suitable number of parallel determination.
In practical analysis, however, an excessively large number of analyses
of one sample is never done, so that the rule holds that every additional
analysis improves the precision of the result. If precision is expressed by
means of the Kaiser-Specker quantity Γ, it holds, for example, that for
$n = 4$ we obtain a mean twice as precise as a single determination, but to
treble the precision requires nine parallel determinations.

Now let us demonstrate by means of some examples the calculation of the standard
deviation and of the standard deviation of the mean value of different sets of analytical
results. Suppose the Kjeldahl method has been used to analyse four kinds of samples
containing approximately 1, 3, 5, and 15 % of nitrogen. For each kind, 12 to 15
individual samples were available, and every sample was analysed twice [50]. This set
is characterized by a large number of samples, each of which has been analysed by
only a small number of determinations. Therefore this is a case in which the estimate
by means of the range is suitable.

Nitrogen, %	R, %	s_R, %	v, %	Γ
1	0.036	0.0320	3.20	31.2
3	0.057	0.0505	1.68	59.5
5	0.062	0.0549	1.10	90.9
15	0.086	0.0762	0.508	196.8

The example illustrates the calculation of the standard deviation s_R from
the mean range R by multiplying by the coefficient $k_n = 0.8862$ $(n = 2)$,
and the calculation of the relative standard deviation, and the Kaiser-Specker
precision characteristic. This example is also interesting in that it illustrates
a frequently encountered fact: when a certain analytical method is being
used, the precision of the results varies with the content of the component
being determined, in such a manner that although absolute precision
(characterized by the value of s_R) decreases with increasing content of the
component (the value of s_R rises), the relative precision, characterized for
example by the value of the coefficient of variation, on the contrary increases
with increasing content of the component in question.

Another example is the calculation of the standard deviation of an individual determination and of the mean of a relatively large number $(n = 16)$ of parallel determinations
of sulphur by the combustion method [42]. The results are the following:

Analysis	Sulphur, % x_i	x_i^2
1	8.60	73.96
2	8.12	65.93
3	8.36	69.89
4	8.67	75.17
5	8.96	80.28
6	8.62	74.30
7	8.61	74.13
8	8.75	76.56
9	8.69	75.52
10	8.72	76.04
11	8.74	76.39
12	9.01	81.18
13	8.50	72.25
14	8.40	70.56
15	8.03	64.48
16	8.30	68.89

$$n = 16 \quad \Sigma\, x_i = 137.08 \quad \Sigma\, x_i^2 = 1175.53$$

The mean value $\bar{x} = \dfrac{1}{16} \Sigma\, x_i = 8.567\%\,S$

$(\Sigma\, x_i)^2 = 18790.9264$

$\dfrac{1}{n} (\Sigma\, x_i)^2 = 1174.43$

$$s = \sqrt{\dfrac{1}{n-1}\left[\Sigma\, x_i^2 - \dfrac{1}{n}(\Sigma\, x_i)^2\right]} = \sqrt{0.0733} = 0.271$$

$$s_{\bar{x}} = \dfrac{1}{\sqrt{16}} \cdot s = \dfrac{0.271}{4} = 0.068$$

The calculation is not too complicated, if a desk calculating machine is used.

The next example illustrates the calculation of the estimate of the parameter σ by means of two methods, i.e. the sum of squares of deviations from the mean, and by means of the range. We have 8 parallel sulphur determinations carried out by oxidation to sulphate, precipitation as barium sulphate, chelatometric titration of excess of barium in alkaline medium, methylthymol blue being used as indicator. The number of determinations $n = 8$ is somewhat too low for the estimate by the sum of squares (in section 4.7 the demand that n be > 15 has been mentioned) while for the estimate by means of the range it is rather large (relative efficiency 0.89). Let us calculate the two estimates and compare them.

Determination	S, %	$(\bar{x} - x_i)$	$(\bar{x} - x_i)^2$
1	19.87	0.08	0.0064
2	19.89	0.06	0.0036
3	19.93	0.02	0.0004
4	19.94	0.01	0.0001
5	19.96	0.01	0.0001
6	19.99	0.04	0.0016
7	20.00	0.05	0.0025
8	20.02	0.07	0.0049

$$\bar{x} = 19.95 \qquad \Sigma\,(\bar{x} - x_i)^2 = 0.0196$$
$$\tilde{x} = 19.95$$
$$R = 20.02 - 19.87 = 0.15$$

1. $s = \sqrt{\dfrac{1}{n-1}\,\Sigma\,(x - x_i)^2} = \sqrt{\dfrac{0.0196}{7}} = 0.05290 \approx 0.053$

$$s_{\bar{x}} = 0.35 \times 0.05290 = 0.18375 \approx 0.184$$

2. $s_R = k_n \cdot R = 0.3512 \times 0.15 = 0.05268 \approx 0.053$

$s_{\bar{x}} = s_R \mid \sqrt{\bar{n}} = 0.35 \times 0.05268 = 0.18438 \approx 0.184$

$$v = \frac{100 s_{\bar{x}}}{\bar{x}} = 0.92\,\%$$

The two estimates of μ, i.e. the mean $\bar{x}$ and the median $\tilde{x}$ are, accidentally, identical and the estimates of σ and the characteristics derived from them agree well when rounded off to three decimal digits.

To round off the discusssion on standard deviation, let us mention the standard deviation of a result y which is calculated from two or more partial results $x_1, x_2, \ldots$, each of which has been determined with a precision characterized by the standard deviation $\sigma_{x_1}, \sigma_{x_2}, \ldots$. The value of the standard deviation of the final result is given by one of the expressions in Table 4.6. This table also gives the equations for the calculation of the standard deviation in cases where y is given e.g. by the sum or difference of the partial results $x_1, x_2, \ldots$, or their product or quotient. Some of these relations will be used in the following sections.

Table 4.6. Calculation of the Standard Deviation of the Final Result y from the Values of the Standard Deviation of Individual Measured Values x_i [5]

General Function: $y = f(x_1; x_2; \ldots; x_n)$	$\sigma_y = \sqrt{\left(\dfrac{\partial y}{\partial x_1}\right)^2 \cdot \sigma_{x_1}^2 + \left(\dfrac{\partial y}{\partial x_2}\right)^2 \cdot \sigma_{x_2}^2 + \ldots}$
Sum and Difference: $y = x_1 \pm x_2$	$\sigma_y = \sqrt{\sigma_{x_1}^2 + \sigma_{x_2}^2}$
Product, Quotient and Power $y = k \cdot x_1 \cdot x_2$	$\sigma_y = k\sqrt{\sigma_{x_1}^2 \cdot x_2^2 + \sigma_{x_2}^2 \cdot x_1^2}$
$y = k \cdot \dfrac{x_1}{x_2}$	$\sigma_y = \dfrac{k}{x_2}\sqrt{\sigma_{x_1}^2 + \dfrac{\sigma_{x_2} \cdot x_1^2}{x_2^2}}$
$y = a + kbx^n$	$\sigma_y = n \cdot k \cdot x^{n-1} \cdot \sigma_x$

4.9 The Gaussian law and the probability of occurrence of an error of given magnitude

The practical significance of the Gaussian law consists in the fact that its validity is assumed in the derivation of statistical methods based on probability principles. This is made possible by the fact that the law expresses the probability of relative frequency of occurrence of an error with respect to the absolute magnitude of the error, and mainly because it allows the probability to be determined of whether or not a certain magnitude of error will be exceeded when a single determination is carried out, or how many individual results among a large number of parallel determinations will (or will not) exceed a given limit of error.

In the graphical illustration of the *Gaussian curve*, e.g. in Fig. 4.4, this probability (or the number of determinations out of the total) may be illustrated as follows: we ask what is the probability of a certain result being subject to an error within the range $(a - b)$, or how many results out of a total number of determinations will lie within this interval. It need not be proved that the wider this interval is from a fixed boundary, the

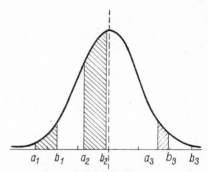

Fig. 4.4. Graphical illustration of probability intervals $(a—b)$ of normally distributed results.

greater the number of results which it will encompass (intervals $a_1 - b_1$ and $a_3 - b_3$ in Fig. 4.4). It is also clear that this number will differ for intervals of equal width, located at different distances from the value of μ: thus for the interval $a_2 - b_2$ it will certainly be greater than for the interval $a_1 - b_1$, because the probability of occurrence of a larger error $d_1 = \mu - a_1$ is far smaller than that of a smaller error, $d_2 = \mu - a_2$. The probability of occurrence of an error in the interval from $-\infty$ to $+\infty$ is, of course, equal to one because it is certain that the result of all determinations will be subject to an error lying somewhere within these limits. In principle, therefore, the probability of occurrence of an error in a given range of magnitude, e.g. between a_1 and b_1 may be expressed by the ratio of an area limited by the x-axis, the Gaussian curve and two perpendiculars through the points a_1 and b_1, to the entire area below the curve. The area is given by an integral: therefore the probability of the error lying within the limits a_1 and b_1 may be expressed by the relation

$$P = \frac{1}{\sqrt{2\pi}} \int_a^b e^{-\frac{1}{2}t^2} . \, dt, \qquad (4.25)$$

where $t = \dfrac{x - \mu}{\sigma}$; $a_1 = \sigma . a$; $b_1 = \sigma . b$.

In practice we are interested in the symmetrical distribution of errors around μ, because the error most frequently considered is $\mu \pm d$. Thus, for an interval of $\mu \pm z . \sigma$ the probability of the error lying within this interval is given by the relation

$$P = \frac{1}{\sqrt{2\pi}} \int_{-z}^{+z} e^{-\frac{1}{2}t^2} . \, dt. \qquad (4.26)$$

The values of this interval are given in Table 4.7. In this table, the probability may be found of the error $d = x_i - \mu$ lying within the interval $\pm z \cdot \sigma$. For example, the probability of the absolute magnitude of the error not exceeding the interval

$$\mu \pm \sigma \quad \text{is} \quad P = 0.6827$$
$$\mu \pm 2\sigma \quad \text{is} \quad P = 0.9454$$
$$\mu \pm 3\sigma \quad \text{is} \quad P = 0.9973 \text{ etc.}$$

In other words, 68.27 % of all results will lie in the interval $\mu \pm \sigma$, 95.45 % in the interval $\mu + 2\sigma$, 99.73 % in the interval $\mu + 3\sigma$ etc. On the other hand, it is possible to search for the magnitude of an error, the probability

Table 4.7. Normal (Gaussian) Distribution. Values of the Integral

$$P = \frac{1}{\sqrt{2\pi}} \int_{-z}^{+z} e^{-\frac{1}{2}t^2} \, dt, \quad \text{where} \quad t = \frac{x - \mu}{\sigma}$$

z	0	1	2	3	4	5	6	7	8	9
0.0	0.0000	0.0080	0.0160	0.0239	0.0319	0.0399	0.0478	0.0558	0.0638	0.0717
0.1	0.0797	0.0876	0.0955	0.1034	0.1113	0.1192	0.1271	0.1350	0.1428	0.1507
0.2	0.1585	0.1663	0.1753	0.1819	0.1897	0.1974	0.2051	0.2127	0.2205	0.2282
0.3	0.2358	0.2434	0.2510	0.2586	0.2661	0.2737	0.2812	0.2886	0.2961	0.3035
0.4	0.3108	0.3182	0.3255	0.3328	0.3401	0.3473	0.3545	0.3616	0.3688	0.3759
0.5	0.3829	0.3899	0.3969	0.4039	0.4177	0.4108	0.4245	0.4313	0.4381	0.4448
0.6	0.4515	0.4581	0.4647	0.4713	0.4778	0.4843	0.4907	0.4971	0.5035	0.5098
0.7	0.5161	0.5223	0.5285	0.5346	0.5407	0.5467	0.5527	0.5587	0.5646	0.5705
0.8	0.5763	0.5821	0.5878	0.5935	0.5991	0.6047	0.6102	0.6157	0.6211	0.6265
0.9	0.6319	0.6372	0.6424	0.6476	0.6528	0.6579	0.6629	0.6680	0.6729	0.6779
1.0	0.6827	0.6875	0.6923	0.6970	0.7017	0.7063	0.7109	0.7154	0.7199	0.7243
1.1	0.7287	0.7330	0.7373	0.7415	0.7457	0.7499	0.7540	0.7580	0.7620	0.7660
1.2	0.7699	0.7737	0.7775	0.7813	0.7850	0.7887	0.7923	0.7959	0.7995	0.8029
1.3	0.8064	0.8098	0.8132	0.8165	0.8198	0.8230	0.8262	0.8293	0.8324	0.8355
1.4	0.8385	0.8415	0.8444	0.8473	0.8501	0.8529	0.8557	0.8584	0.8611	0.8638
1.5	0.8664	0.8690	0.8715	0.8740	0.8764	0.8789	0.8812	0.8836	0.8859	0.8882
1.6	0.8904	0.8926	0.8948	0.8969	0.8990	0.9011	0.9031	0.9051	0.9070	0.9090
1.7	0.9109	0.9127	0.9146	0.9164	0.9181	0.9199	0.9216	0.9233	0.9249	0.9265
1.8	0.9281	0.9297	0.9312	0.9327	0.9342	0.9357	0.9371	0.9385	0.9399	0.9412
1.9	0.9426	0.9439	0.9451	0.9464	0.9476	0.9488	0.9500	0.9512	0.9523	0.9534
2.0	0.9545	0.9556	0.9566	0.9576	0.9586	0.9596	0.9606	0.9615	0.9625	0.9633
2.1	0.9643	0.9651	0.9660	0.9668	0.9676	0.9684	0.9692	0.9700	0.9707	0.9715
2.2	0.9722	0.9729	0.9736	0.9743	0.9749	0.9756	0.9762	0.9768	0.9774	0.9780
2.3	0.9786	0.9791	0.9797	0.9802	0.9807	0.9812	0.9817	0.9822	0.9827	0.9832
2.4	0.9836	0.9840	0.9845	0.9849	0.9853	0.9857	0.9861	0.9865	0.9869	0.9872
2.5	0.9876	0.9879	0.9883	0.9886	0.9889	0.9892	0.9895	0.9898	0.9901	0.9904
2.6	0.9907	0.9909	0.9912	0.9915	0.9917	0.9920	0.9922	0.9924	0.9926	0.9929
2.7	0.9931	0.9933	0.9935	0.9937	0.9939	0.9940	0.9942	0.9944	0.9946	0.9947
2.8	0.9949	0.9950	0.9952	0.9953	0.9955	0.0056	0.9958	0.9959	0.9960	0.9961
2.9	0.9963	0.9964	0.9965	0.9966	0.9967	0.9968	0.9969	0.9970	0.9971	0.9972
3.0	0.9973	0.9974	0.9975	0.9976	0.9976	0.9977	0.9978	0.9979	0.9979	0.9980

of which is set at will. For example, for $P = 0.5$ the tables show, by inter-polation, $z = 0.6745$: this means that for an error of 0.6745σ (roughly $2\sigma/3$) the probability that it will be exceeded is equal to the probability that it will not be exceeded, i.e. one half of all results will be subject to a larger, one half to a smaller error.

For a practical measure of reproducibility it is possible to use an error with a preselected probability of not being exceeded. This measure is more illustrative than the standard deviation. For example, a measure of precision frequently used in physical measurements, is the probable error ϑ for $P = 0.5$, already shown to be 0.6745σ. In other cases it may be of more advantage to select for z a whole number, and to state the error with its related probability: in analytical chemistry the error of $\pm 2\sigma$ with the probability $P = 0.9545$ is used most often, or $\pm 3\sigma$ with the probability $P = 0.9973$. These measures of reproducibility have the advantage that at the same time they illustrate rather well the probability with which it may be expected that the experimental results will not exceed a calculated difference from the true value. It should here be kept in mind that the more certain we wish to be that a given error will not be exceeded for an individual result, the greater will be the absolute magnitude of the error; thus the results become less precise. Since the probability of large errors is low a large increase in the value of z brings about only a slight increase of the probability that the error will not be exceeded. Thus 34.13 % of the results lie in the interval between μ and $\mu + \sigma$, while only 13.59 % lie in the interval from $\mu + \sigma$ to $\mu + 2\sigma$, and only 2.14 % of all results lie in the interval $\mu + 2\sigma$ to $\mu + 3\sigma$, the remaining 0.14 % of the total of 50 % of results greater than μ being found in the interval from $\mu + 3\sigma$ to ∞.

This also brings us to the solution of the question which we asked earlier: can the precision of results be a criterion of their accuracy? The greater the precision of the results, the narrower is the interval $\pm 2\sigma$ for a present value of z. This, however, does not mean that the results obtained will agree to the same extent with the real value, since the considerations above have been derived on the assumption that only random errors are present and systematic errors are not considered at all. Thus, precision is a measure of accuracy only if systematic errors are eliminated by a suitable selection of the analytical procedure and if the analyses are carried out with such care that the occurrence of gross errors need not be taken into account.

4.10 The reliability interval

Estimates of the parameter μ made by calculating the arithmetic mean are subject to the disadvantage that this estimate does not express the reliability with which it has been determined. It cannot be assumed in practice that the true value of the content of a component in the sample analysed agrees exactly with the mean of the results obtained, x, as it is known from experience that if several more analyses were done, and the mean $\bar{x}$ calculated again, the new value would differ somewhat from the previous value. This difficulty is common to all point-type estimates, in which the parameter to be estimated is replaced by a single value. It is true that the mean x is a consistent estimate, but in practical analysis very large numbers of parallel determinations cannot be performed. It is therefore sometimes better to determine an interval within which it is highly probable that the true value lies. This interval is called *the reliability interval*, and the probability selected is called *the reliability coefficient*, denoted by $(1 - \alpha)$. The reliability interval is an example of *interval-type estimates*.

If we knew the value of the standard deviation σ with sufficient precision (as in the case of a method already statistically tested), this reliability interval for $(1 - \alpha)$ could be expressed as $\bar{x} \pm z\sigma$, z being the coefficient for the Gaussian distribution as used in Table 4.7. In most cases, however, the value of σ is unknown, and must be replaced by the estimate s, and generally it is impossible to carry out a number of determinations large enough to allow the value of σ in the interval $\bar{x} \pm z \cdot \sigma$ to be replaced by the value of s without running the risk of depreciating the accuracy of the statistical evaluation. Therefore in principle two procedures are possible for the calculation of the reliability interval from a small number of parallel determinations with normal probability distribution. In one the estimate of σ is calculated, and since this is a value of reliability, it is multiplied by the "Student" coefficient t [92]. This coefficient replaces the Gaussian coefficient z in cases where σ has been replaced by its estimate. The probability distribution of this coefficient t was derived by the English statistician GOSSET and published by him under the pseudonym "STUDENT". It is a symmetrical distribution dependent on the number of determinations employed, n. It is similar to the Gaussian normal distribution, which it approaches for $n \to \infty$. The second way used, with a small number of determinations, sets out from the range R as was done in the calculation of the estimate of σ.

The "Student" distribution will be discussed frequently in the following sections. Moreover, it should be mentioned that the significance of this distribution does not lie only in the fact that it permits a calculation of the reliability interval for the arithmetic mean $\bar{x}$ even if the parameter is not known precisely and must be replaced by the estimate s. For the present, let us mention solely the relations for different cases of calculations of the reliability interval, L_1 being the lower and L_2 the upper limit of the reliability interval.

With the use of the Gaussian distribution, i.e. if the value of the parameter σ is known, the reliability interval is calculated from

$$L_{1,2} = \bar{x} \pm \frac{z}{\sqrt{n}} \cdot \sigma \qquad (4.27)$$

the value of z being given in Table 4.7 for a given level of significance. Using the Student distribution, i.e. estimating the standard deviation from the results from which the mean $\bar{x}$ has been calculated, the reliability interval is obtained according to [57] by means of the relationship

$$L_{1,2} = \bar{x} \pm \frac{t}{\sqrt{n}} \cdot s \qquad (4.28)$$

Either the value of the coefficient t is found in the table of critical values of the Student t-distribution (Table 4.10, page 109) or, more simply, values of z/n or $t/\sqrt{n}$ are taken from Table 4.8.

Table 4.8. Values of $\dfrac{z}{\sqrt{n}}$ from the Gaussian

Distribution and $\dfrac{t}{\sqrt{n}}$ from the Student Distribution

	$\dfrac{z}{\sqrt{n}}$		$\dfrac{t}{\sqrt{n}}$	
n				
$(1 - \alpha) =$	0.95	0.997	0.95	0.997
2	1.38	2.12	9.00	166
3	1.13	1.73	2.48	11.1
4	0.98	1.50	1.59	4.61
5	0.88	1.34	1.24	2.96
6	0.80	1.22	1.05	2.25
7	0.75	1.13	0.92	1.85
8	0.69	1.06	0.84	1.60
9	0.65	1.00	0.77	1.42
10	0.62	0.95	0.72	1.29
25	0.39	0.60	0.41	0.67

In practice, the determination of the reliability interval by means of the range is found to be more useful. On the one hand, this procedure is very simple, on the other hand it can also be used for very small numbers of determinations. The calculation is based on the relationship

$$L_{1,2} = \bar{x} \pm K_n \cdot R \qquad (4.29)$$

In this equation, $R = x_n - x_1$ is the range, and the value of K_n is found in Table 4.9 for a selected significance level $(1 - \alpha) = 0.95$ or 0.99. In principle these are rounded-off critical values of LORD'S μ_0-test, which will be discussed later in a different context. The practical significance of such a simple method of calculating the reliability interval need not be stressed.

Let us now discuss the values of K_n for different values of n. It is clear at first sight that K_n values decrease with rising values of n very rapidly at first, then more slowly and finally only very slightly. This means that increasing the number of parallel determinations from $n = 2$ to $n = 3$ causes the reliability interval to narrow considerably, i.e. increases the reliability of the result, while an increase from $n = 5$ to $n = 6$ has practically no influence on the width of the reliability interval (especially, if the sixth result falls outside the other five and increases the range). On considering the absolute values of K_n, e.g. for $1 - \alpha = 0.95$, we find that for $n = 3$ or 4 the reliability interval is roughly twice the range, and for $n = 5$ is equal to the range.

Table 4.9. Values of the Coefficient K_n for Calculating the Reliability Interval from the Range [46]

	K_n	
n		
	$(1 - \alpha) = 0.95$	0.99
2	6.4	31.8
3	1.3	3.01
4	0.92	1.32
5	0.51	0.84
6	0.40	0.63
7	0.33	0.51
8	0.29	0.43
9	0.26	0.37
10	0.23	0.33

Let us illustrate the calculation of the reliability interval from the range by means of an example. Five nitrogen analyses have been carried out on the same sample by the Kjeldahl method: the following results were obtained:

$$N, \%$$
$$8.35$$
$$8.21$$
$$8.32$$
$$8.30$$
$$8.37$$

$$\bar{x} = 8.31$$
$$\bar{R} = 8.37 - 8.21 = 0.16\%; \quad n = 5$$

The reliability interval, in which the true result lies with a probability of $1 - \alpha = 0.95$, is $8.31 \pm (0.16 \times 0.51)$ i.e. $8.23 - 8.39 \% N$: the interval width is $L_2 - L_1 = 8.39 - 8.23 = 0.16 \%$.

If, however, the reliability interval were calculated for two results of nitrogen analyses carried out by the same method (the results agreeing very well), e.g.

$$N, \%$$
$$7.06$$
$$7.08$$

$$\bar{x} = 7.07$$
$$\bar{R} = 7.08 - 7.06 = 0.02 \%; \quad n = 2$$

the reliability interval would be $7.07 \pm (0.02 \times 6.4)$; i.e. $6.94 - 7.20 \% N$: the interval width would now be 0.26. Thus, although the results agree well mutually, there is no guarantee of outstanding accuracy even if it may be assumed that there is no systematic error involved: the reason is the fact that the number of determinations is too small. If a third analysis were done with a result of $7.01 \% N$, the reliability interval would be narrowed, even though this result differs somewhat from the preceding two:

$$N, \%$$
$$7.06$$
$$7.08$$
$$7.01$$

$$\bar{x} = 7.05$$
$$R = 7.08 - 7.01 = 0.07\%; \quad n = 3$$

Now the reliability interval is $7.05 \pm (0.07 \times 1.3) = 6.96 - 7.14 \% N$, the interval width is 0.18%.

In practical analytical chemistry one is used to expressing errors in per cent of the overall content: thus the width of the reliability interval may be expressed by means of the *relative width of the reliability interval*, denoted by i:

$$i = \frac{L_2 - L_1}{\bar{x}} \tag{4.30}$$

and for the calculation using the range,

$$i = \frac{2 \cdot K_n \cdot R}{\bar{x}} \cdot 100 \tag{4.31}$$

Thus for the last example given, $i = \dfrac{0.18 \times 100}{7.05} = 2.55\%$.

It may frequently happen in practice that we have to be satisfied with a relative reliability interval width of up to 5 %, and sometimes, mainly with low concentrations and small numbers of parallel determinations, i values $> 10\%$ have to be accepted.

The reliability interval represents an interval in which the true result lies with high probability, if none but random errors are present: thus it expresses, to a certain extent, the imprecision of the results. The width of the reliability interval or, better, the relative width of the reliability interval, is a measure of the magnitude of this imprecision. The significances of the reliability interval or of its width in terms of a measure of imprecision is elucidated best by means of the following section.

4.11 The amount of information obtainable

It has been mentioned several times in the preceding sections that some information is gained from each determination. Let us now attempt to apply some relations and concepts from the theory of information in order to determine, at least in a semiquantitative manner, the *amount of information* gained from a given determination, which may either be a single determination or a result obtained as the mean value from several parallel determinations. The point of greatest interest is to find the conditions under which the amount of information thus obtained will be maximal.

The amount of information (I) obtained by observation or measurement is given by the relation [2, 3]

$$I = k \cdot \log_b \frac{P_0}{P} \tag{4.32}$$

where P_0 is the imprecision, i.e. the number of possibilities of equal probability existing before the observation, P is the imprecision after the observation. The constant k and especially the base of the logarithms used, b, determine the unit in which the amount of information is expressed: e.g. for $\log_{10}$ the unit is the "*hartley*", for the natural logarithm $\log_e$ it is the so-called *natural digit* and for $\log_2$ the *binary digit* or "*bit*". Equation 4.32 may be utilized in qualitative analysis, where it may be employed for example to find the amount of information to be gained from performing a given qualitative reaction, by means of which the presence of certain components of the sample may be established or excluded. In quantitative analysis, however, it is preferable to consider the imprecision not as a number of possibilities but as an interval of values within which the true, accurate concentration value of the component in question may lie before and after the measurement is performed. The imprecision P_0 is equal to 100 in the case of chemical analysis, since the content of the component determined must lie between 0 and 100%, while the imprecision P after the analysis is given by the width of the interval in which, according to the result of the analysis, the true value of the component must lie. One of the quantities which can be substituted for P is the absolute width of the reliability interval, so

$$I = k \cdot \log_b \frac{100}{z \cdot \sigma_{\bar{x}}} \qquad (4.33)$$

The value of z will be found, for a preselected significance level, in tables of the Gaussian distribution. It is also possible to start out from the SHANNON relationship, which may be written for the case of a continuous distribution [2] as

$$I = \int p(x) \cdot \log_e p(x) \cdot dx \qquad (4.34)$$

and for the probability density we may substitute from the Gaussian law

$$p(x) = \frac{1}{\sigma \sqrt{2\pi}} \cdot e^{-\frac{1}{2}\left(\frac{x-\mu}{\sigma}\right)^2} \qquad (4.35)$$

On simplifying, we obtain the expression

$$I = \log_e \frac{100}{\sigma \sqrt{2\pi e}} \qquad (4.36)$$

which is, in fact, Eq. 4.33 with the values $k = 1$, $b = e$, and $z = \sqrt{2\pi e} = 4.13274$. This value of z is quite acceptable, as the Gaussian law shows that 95.9 % of all results lie within the interval $\mu \pm \frac{1}{2}\sqrt{2\pi e}$. In this case the amount of information is expressed in natural digits.

When n parallel determinations are being done and the result is expressed as their mean, the relation is

$$I = \log_e \frac{100\sqrt{n}}{\sigma \sqrt{2\pi e}} \qquad (4.37)$$

It follows from Eq. 4.37 that the amount of information will be the greater, the more parallel analyses are carried out and the more precise these analyses are, i.e. the lower is the value of σ. The greatest influence is here exerted by the precision. When a second parallel determination is carried out, the amount of information is increased by 0.345 natural digits, a third determination means an increase of 0.205 natural digits, and so on. Excessive numbers of determinations bring about only slight increases of the amount of information. In considering the number of determinations, it is also possible to determine the *redundance*

$$\varrho = \frac{I_{max} - I}{I_{max}} \qquad (4.38)$$

where I is the information actually gained and I_{max} is the maximum information obtainable from n determinations. Calculating the value of I from Eq. 4.37 and noting the relationship $I_{max} = n \cdot I_1$, where I_1 is the amount of information which can be obtained from one determination, we find that redundance rises with rising number of determinations n. Redundance represents the excess of effort exerted in comparison to the case in which a maximum of information would be obtained with the same effort. Redundance, however, is not—at least to a certain extent—useless effort. It must be kept in mind that all the relationships considered are only valid if the results are subject to no systematic errors but random ones. Systematic errors may be avoided by a suitable modification of the analytical procedure, but the occurrence of a gross error can never be excluded, and for this reason a large number of parallel analyses is carried out, and the individual results are compared in order to find out whether any outlying results are involved. The repeated (parallel) determinations thus represent only a slight increase in the overall amount of information obtainable, but this is compensated by the increased redundance which again makes it easier to distinguish any results which might possibly be subject to a gross error.

4.12　Deviations from the Gaussian law of error distribution

The Gaussian law of error distribution is a mathematical model of the continuous distribution of results which are subject to random errors only. It has been derived on the assumption that every measured value is influenced by an infinite number of infinitely small elementary errors which may be added together or which may compensate each other. Obviously the precise validity of the Gaussian law in the range from $-\infty$ to $+\infty$ can never be assumed: when the validity of the normal distribution law is spoken of its satisfaction within a region of roughly $\mu \pm 3\sigma$ is what is really meant.

The assumptions with which this law has been derived need not however be satisfied in practical analyses, and thus various deviations from the normal distribution may be encountered even in the vicinity of μ. These may, for example, be *deviations from "peak narrowness"* with maintained symmetry of the distribution: these will not be discussed, however, as they are irrelevant to the problems in question. Far more important are deviations from the symmetry of the distribution; in some cases distributions with several peaks may also be obtained.

Non-symmetrical distributions will be encountered mainly in those cases where errors of a given sign are, for some reason, more probable than errors of the opposite sign. For example slight asymmetry is sometimes found in titration, the distribution being elongated in the direction towards higher values, because in titrations with the use of indicators there is a greater tendency to slight over-titration than to under-titration. The situation is similar in trace analysis, where components are being determined close to the limit of detection and the results obtained cannot be lower than "zero". Here an asymmetric distribution, rather elongated towards greater values, is the rule. On the other hand, PLŠKO [80] has found by repeated photometric measurement of spectral lines, that there is a tendency to asymmetry in the opposite direction, because results tend to be lower.

Among non-symmetrical distributions, the significant ones are those where not the measured value, but one of its functions (transformations), is distributed normally; e.g. the *lognormal distribution*, which is of great

importance in analytical chemistry. In this distribution the logarithm of
the variable, i.e. the transformation $X_i = \log x_i$, has a normal distribution.
The shape of the curve which represents the lognormal distribution is
shown in Fig. 4.5, compared with the normal distribution. The parameters
of the lognormal distribution are estimated from the logarithms of the
measured quantities or of the final results by means of the well known
relationships. For example, the estimate of the parameter μ is

$$\bar{X} = \frac{1}{n} \Sigma X_i, \quad \text{i.e.} \quad \log \bar{x}_g = \frac{1}{n} \Sigma \log x_i;$$

$$\bar{x}_g = \sqrt[n]{x_1 \cdot x_2 \ldots x_n} \tag{4.39}$$

$\bar{x}_g$ being the *geometric mean*. This geometric mean is always smaller than
the arithmetic mean $(\bar{x}_a)$, the difference being the greater, the greater the

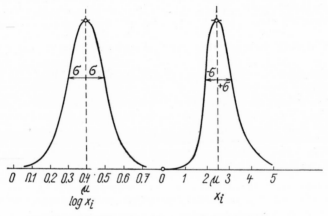

FIG. 4.5. Normal and lognormal distribution.

degree of assymetry of the distribution. The estimate of the parameter σ
i.e. s_{1_g} is obtained quite similarly, e.g. by means of Eq. 4.13 (p. 86).
In the case of a non-symmetrical distribution the standard deviation is
obviously calculated separately for the part of the curve above the mean
value, i.e. $+s = \log s_{1_g}$, while the standard deviation for the part of the
curve below the mean value is $-s = \log \dfrac{1}{s_{1_g}}$. This must be kept in mind,
especially when calculating the confidence interval, which obviously is not
symmetrical about the mean. Estimates calculated from the range cannot,
of course, be used here.

In practical analytical chemistry, two cases are possible in which
a lognormal distribution must be assumed:

(1) the quantities measured depend on a quantity which has normal
distribution, the relation being a logarithmic one,

(2) the measured quantities are close to a theoretical or natural limit.
For this reason, the lognormal distribution occurs for example with results
of trace analyses or in emission spectrography, where the dependence
between the content of the element determined and the blackening of the

spectral line is a logarithmic one (see the Scheibe-Lomakin equation, p. 68). The assumption of the lognormal distribution has also been empirically proved to be correct in both cases.

As an example let us calculate the mean value of the results of the determination of nickel in potassium hydroxide by emission spectrography.

Determination: Ni, %

	x_i	$\log x_i$	$(x_i - \bar{x}_a)^2$	$(\log x_i - \log \bar{x}_g)^2$
1	1.3×10^{-4}	—3.886	10.24×10^{-8}	0.1747
2	2.0×10^{-4}	—3.699	6.25×10^{-8}	0.0533
3	5.8×10^{-4}	—3.237	1.69×10^{-8}	0.0533
4	8.9×10^{-4}	—3.051	19.36×10^{-8}	0.1739
Σ	18.0×10^{-4}	—13.873	37.54×10^{-8}	0.4552

for $n = 4$, $\alpha = 0.95$, $t = 3.182$

A. Normal distribution:

Arithmetic mean: $\bar{x}_a = \dfrac{1}{4} \times 18.0 \times 10^{-4} = 4.5 \times 10^{-4} \%\ \text{Ni}$

Standard deviation: $s = \sqrt{\dfrac{1}{3} \times 37.54 \times 10^{-8}} = 3.54 \times 10^{-4}$

Confidence interval: $L_{1,2} = 4.5 \times 10^{-4} \pm \sqrt{\dfrac{1}{4}} \times 3.182 \times 3.54 \times 10^{-4}$

Upper limit of the confidence interval: $L_2 = 1.0 \times 10^{-3} \%\ \text{Ni}$
The lower limit of the confidence interval cannot be determined ($L_1 < 0$)

B. Lognormal distribution:

Geometric mean: $\log \bar{x}_g = -\dfrac{1}{4} \times 13.873 = 0.4682 - 4$

$\bar{x}_g = 2.9 \times 10^{-4} \%\ \text{Ni}$

Standard deviation: $\log s_{1g} = \sqrt{\dfrac{1}{3} \times 0.4552} = \pm 0.3895$

$s_{1g} \begin{cases} 2,452 \\ 0.408 \end{cases}$

Confidence interval: $L_{1,2} = \bar{x}_g \pm \dfrac{t \cdot s}{\sqrt{n}}$

$L_1 = 1.7 \times 10^{-4}$
$L_2 = 1.0 \times 10^{-3}$

In this example the calculation of the standard deviation is included for illustration only. Obviously for $n = 4$ a reliable estimate of the parameter σ can hardly be obtained in this way.

One of the distributions elongated in the direction towards the lower values is the one in which the reciprocal values of the quantity measured have a normal distribution. It is of less importance in analytical chemistry than is the lognormal distribution. The calculation with the transformation $X_i = k/x_i$, k being a suitable constant differing from zero, is quite similar to the calculation of the normal Gaussian distribution.

Another case which may be encountered is a "compound" distribution which—in the extreme case—may have two peaks. This is usually due to non-homogenity of the sample or of the results (e.g. results of the analysis of the sample, carried out in two different laboratories, being grouped together, etc). Obviously no parameters can be calculated from such a distribution.

Let us briefly also mention a graphical method of determining the shape of the distribution of results, using probability paper with the probability scale plotted on the ordinate axis (Fig. 4.6). The results are arranged in

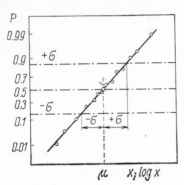

FIG. 4.6. Graphical testing of normality of distribution.

order of magnitude and on the probability graph the value of $y_1 = 100/2n$ is plotted for x_1, n being the overall number of results. For every following point the ordinate value plotted is $y_j = y_{j-1} + 100/n$. The points thus obtained are joined together. If the distribution is truly normal, a straight line will be obtained. In quite the same way, a lognormal distribution may be tested by means of graph paper with a logarithmic scale on one axis and a probability scale on the other. The same holds for any other distribution in which after transformation the transformed variable has a normal distribution. Besides simplicity, this method has the advantage that if a deviation from the normal (or lognormal, etc) distribution is found, it is at least roughly possible to determine the kind of deviation concerned. Deviations of "peak narrowness" are generally not very grave, as already mentioned, and they do not require any special modification of statistical methods. These deviations are recognized by a symmetrical S-shaped curve. A non-symmetrical distribution will give a non-symmetrical curve. Some details of the possibilities of applying this graphical test will be found in the literature [10].

It should be mentioned in conclusion that small deviations from the Gaussian distribution may be expected in the majority of real distributions of analytical results, and they need be no cause for fear that a grave error is being committed by the use of statistical methods based on this distribution. If a large deviation is detected, especially asymmetry of the distribution, it is possible to attempt by means of a suitable transformation to find a mathematical model which will better express the actual distribution. A suitable mathematical model of the distribution, however, can be sought only if sufficient experimental material is available. If the deviations from the normal distribution are great, and we do not succeed in finding a suitable mathematical model, there still remains the possibility of using the so-called non-parametric statistical methods, which are not based on the assumption of any mathematically defined distribution. Some of these will be discussed in a later section. The problem of the real distribution of the results of chemical analyses has been investigated, e.g. by CLANCEY [43], DOERFFEL [8], NALIMOV [25], SPRENT [91] and WOKROJ [100]. The distribution of the results of spectral analysis has been studied by AHRENS [1], PLŠKO [80, 81], EHRLICH and GERBATSCH [59, 60] etc.

4.13 Student's *t*-distribution

In the majority of practical applications, the parameter is replaced by its asymptotically efficient estimate, i.e. one which may have quite a great variability if only a small number of determinations is made. Therefore, in cases where a small number of results is to be evaluated [97], the normal distribution is replaced by the STUDENT *t* *distribution* [92] which represents the distribution of the quotient of a quantity of normal distribution and of a quantity which has a distribution of the standard deviation, the two quantities being independent of each other. This symmetrical distribution depends on a single parameter, i.e. on *n,* differing from the normal distribution by having a greater frequency of larger errors and a smaller frequency of smaller errors. With increasing number of determinations *n* it approaches the normal distribution, converting into this at $n \to \infty$ (i.e. it is asymptotically normal); for $n \ge 30$ the *t* distribution may quite well be replaced by the normal distribution. The Student and Gaussian distributions are compared in Fig. 4.7.

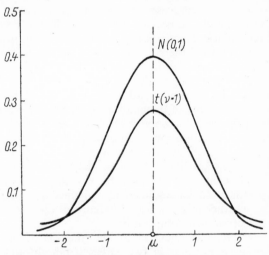

FIG. 4.7. Normal (*N*) and Student's (*t*) distribution.

Let us now discuss the practical application of Student's distribution. On the one hand, as already mentioned, it permits the calculation of the confidence interval for the unknown parameter μ, if only an estimate of the parameter σ is available, with the possibility of using either the normal or the lognormal distributions.

More important, however, is the fact that Student's distribution may have, for example, the following characteristics

$$t = \frac{(\bar{x} - \mu)\sqrt{n}}{s} \tag{4.40}$$

or

$$t = \frac{\bar{x}_A - \bar{x}_B}{\sqrt{s_A^2 + s_B^2}}. \tag{4.41}$$

These characteristics always include (i) the standard deviation and (ii) a difference, e.g. the difference between the estimate of the parameter μ and its true value, or the difference of two means, i.e. quantities having a normal distribution. This permits the accuracy of the mean to be tested with the first criterion (Eq. 4.40), and the difference of two means to be tested with the second criterion (Eq. 4.41).

Thus the t-test may be used in the following cases.

(1) A test is used to find out whether a given analytical method is subject to a systematic error, or whether it gives accurate results. The procedure involves analysing a sample of known composition, and comparison of the t-values to see whether the result obtained differs from the true content more than is necessary if only random errors occur. This procedure may be used, for example, in tests by means of which the accurate functioning of elementary analysis equipment is to be determined, or in the verification of any method by means of standard samples, etc.

(2). In other cases it may be known that a method affords accurate results, and a substance is to be identified by comparison of the composition determined experimentally with the composition calculated. The case is quite clear if there is very good agreement between the results and the calculated composition, or on the contrary, if the composition found differs totally from the assumed one: if, however, the difference is only small, it must be decided whether this difference may be explained by random errors of the analysis or by disagreement between the experimental and theoretical composition. The use of the results of elementary analysis for the identification of an organic substance may well serve as an example. In other cases again, analysis by means of an accurate method is used to check the quality of some product by determining the content of a given component, and it must be decided whether the difference from the specification values may be explained by an error of the determination, or whether this is a true difference of the composition of the product from the prescribed composition.

(3) Results obtained by the analysis of one sample by means of two different methods in two different laboratories, with two instruments etc, are to be compared, or on the other hand results are to be compared which have been obtained by the analysis of different samples with the same method, and it is to be decided whether results for the two methods or the two samples may be assumed to be virtually identical.

From these facts follows the great significance of applications of the t-test, and therefore several of the following sections will be devoted to these applications.

First let us briefly discuss statistical testing. In practice, without the use of statistics, we would judge (in the cases mentioned) whether there is a large or small difference between the concentrations calculated and found or between individual results: a small difference may be explained by random errors in the set of results, a large one cannot be explained in this way. There are some obvious questions: when is a difference "small", and when is it "large"? Clearly one and the same difference, e.g. 0.1 %, may be "small" in one case and "large" in another, while one analyst will regard the difference between the calculated and found values as "small" and permissible, while another may think it is "large". Thus, much depends, if not on the personal views, then certainly on the experience and "severity" of the one who judges the result, and in this way the opinion is subjective.

In the application of statistical tests the procedure involves the substitution of the values found into a mathematical equation for the calculation of a certain criterion, and we look for the probability of the criterion attaining

Table 4.10. Student's t distribution

ν \ α	0.9	0.8	0.6	0.5	0.4	0.2	0.1	0.05	0.01
1	0.158	0.325	0.727	1.000	1.376	3.078	6.314	12.706	63.657
2	0.142	0.289	0.617	0.816	1.061	1.886	2.920	4.303	9.925
3	0.137	0.277	0.584	0.765	0.978	1.638	2.353	3.182	5.841
4	0.134	0.271	0.569	0.741	0.941	1.533	2.132	2.776	4.604
5	0.132	0.267	0.559	0.727	0.920	1.476	2.015	2.571	4.032
6	0.131	0.265	0.553	0.718	0.906	1.440	1.943	2.447	3.707
7	0.130	0.263	0.549	0.711	0.896	1.415	1.895	2.365	3.499
8	0.130	0.262	0.546	0.706	0.889	1.397	1.860	2.306	3.355
9	0.129	0.261	0.543	0.703	0.883	1.383	1.833	2.262	3.250
10	0.129	0.260	0.542	0.700	0.879	1.372	1.812	2.228	3.169
11	0.129	0.260	0.540	0.697	0.876	1.363	1.796	2.201	3.106
12	0.128	0.259	0.539	0.695	0.873	1.356	1.782	2.179	3.055
13	0.128	0.259	0.538	0.694	0.870	1.350	1.771	2.160	3.012
14	0.128	0.258	0.537	0.692	0.868	1.345	1.761	2.145	2.977
15	0.128	0.258	0.536	0.691	0.866	1.341	1.753	2.131	2.947
16	0.128	0.258	0.535	0.690	0.865	1.337	1.746	2.120	2.921
17	0.128	0.257	0.534	0.689	0.863	1.333	1.740	2.110	2.898
18	0.127	0.257	0.534	0.688	0.862	1.330	1.734	2.101	2.878
19	0.127	0.257	0.533	0.688	0.861	1.328	1.729	2.093	2.861
20	0.127	0.257	0.533	0.687	0.860	1.325	1.725	2.086	2.845
25	0.127	0.256	0.531	0.684	0.856	1.316	1.708	2.060	2.787
30	0.127	0.256	0.530	0.683	0.854	1.310	1.697	2.042	2.750
∞	0.12566	0.25335	0.52440	0.67449	0.84162	1.28155	1.64485	1.95996	2.57582

that value which we have obtained by calculation. To do this we need tables which give the critical values for different probabilities, called in this case confidence coefficients. Whether the value of a test criterion may be explained by the presence of random errors only, can be decided in two ways. The first, described mainly in the older studies, was based on the selection of a certain confidence coefficient as the level of significance for which the experimental and tabulated values were compared. This method, rather widely used even now, has one grave disadvantage: the decision is influenced by rather an arbitrary level of significance. Moreover this method does not consider the fact that there is a continuous transition between perfect agreement and absolute disagreement. For these reasons, the following procedure is better [13]: no significance level is selected, but instead we find in the tables the probability of the test characteristic being able to attain the calculated value if random errors only are involved. Thus it is possible to decide, e.g. that for a confidence coefficient of $(1 - \alpha) > 0.99$ the difference will be regarded as statistically *highly significant*, for $(1 - \alpha) = 0.99$ to 0.95 it will be *statistically significant* and for $(1 - \alpha) < 0.95$ it will be taken as *insignificant*. The two procedures will be illustrated in the following section.

4.14 Comparison of the mean with the expected value

The comparison of the mean value of several parallel determinations with the expected value may have two purposes: either we know the true content of the component analysed and wish to find whether the analytical method employed gives accurate results subject to random errors only, or we compare the results found with the expected composition. In both cases the concern is, in principle, with determining whether the difference between the experimental and the true composition may be due to random errors. The comparison may be carried out by means of the t-test by substituting the mean value found for x in Eq. 4.40, substituting the expected value for μ and the estimate of the standard deviation (calculated according to Eq. 4.13 from the same data from which the mean value has been calculated) for s. The value of t thus obtained is compared with tabulated critical values of t for the number of degrees of freedom $v = n - 1$. The number of degrees of freedom is one less than the number of determinations, because one mean value occurs in the equation [4, 14].

The application of Student's t-test will now be illustrated by a specific example of a study of the accuracy of results of Kjeldahl nitrogen determinations. Analyses of pure benzanilide samples were repeated five times [50].

Benzanilide: calculated nitrogen content $\mu = 7.10 \% N$

Results found

% N	$(\bar{x} - x_i)$	$(\bar{x} - x_i)^2$
7.11	—0.04	0.0016
7.08	—0.01	0.0001
7.06	+0.01	0.0001
7.06	+0.01	0.0001
7.04	+0.03	0.0009
$\bar{x} = 7.07$		$\Sigma(x - x_i)^2 = 0.0028$

$$s = \sqrt{\frac{0.0028}{4}} = 0.0264$$

$$t = \frac{(\mu - \bar{x}) \cdot \sqrt{n}}{s} = \frac{(7.10 - 7.07) \cdot \sqrt{5}}{0.0264} = 2.541$$

Let us now compare this value with the tabulated critical values t_k. For $\nu = n - 1 = 4$ degrees of freedom we find in Table 4.10 the following values

$\alpha =$	0.50	0.40	0.20	0.10	0.05	0.01
$\nu = 4$	0.741	0.941	1.533	2.132	2.776	4.604

According to the older method of decision we should now select a certain significance level, e.g. $1 - \alpha = 0.95$ ($\alpha = 0.05$), and compare the calculated and tabulated values: $t = 2.531 < t_k = 2.776$, i.e. the calculated value is lower than the critical one at the given significance level, and the difference of 0.03 % may be ascribed to the presence of random errors. With the second method we should find that the calculated value lies between the tabulated values for $(1 - \alpha) = 0.90$ and 0.95 and the difference thus may be assumed to be statistically insignificant.

We come to the same conclusion in both cases, but the method differs by means of which a decision has been achieved. In the first case we have decided on a certain significance level above which we would no longer be willing to accept the difference as being statistically insignificant. The value of the calculated criterion is lower than a value corresponding to the selected significance level, and we therefore accept it as being statistically insignificant. In the second case we have found that the calculated criterion value has a magnitude which corresponds to a probability of about 0.10 to 0.05 that the difference was caused by random errors. This probability is not small enough to force us to assume the difference to be statistically significant, and therefore we accept it as statistically insignificant in this case also.

4.15 Comparison of the results of two different methods

Beside comparison of the mean results of analyses with the true concentration μ, Student's t-test can also be employed to compare the mean values obtained with two different methods. The mutual agreement of the two means may be tested by means of a criterion, expressed in this case by the relation

$$t = \frac{\bar{x}_A - \bar{x}_B}{\sqrt{\dfrac{(n_A + n_B)(n_A s_A^2 + n_B s_B^2)}{n_A n_B (n_A + n_B - 2)}}} \qquad (4.42)$$

where $\bar{x}_A$, $\bar{x}_B$ are the arithmetic means of the results of the two methods; s_A and s_B are estimates of the standard deviations and n_A, n_B are the numbers of parallel determinations carried out by the methods A and B respectively. The value thus calculated is again compared with the tabulated value for the number of degrees of freedom $\nu = (n_A + n_B - 2)$. Here the number of degrees of freedom is decreased by two, because the concern is with the difference of two means, and one degree of freedom is subtracted for every mean [4, 14].

If the same number of determinations is carried out with both methods, i.e. $n_A = n_B = n$, the criterion is reduced to

$$t = \frac{\bar{x}_A - \bar{x}_B}{\sqrt{\dfrac{s_A^2 + s_B^2}{n - 1}}} \qquad (4.43)$$

the number of degrees of freedom being $v = 2n - 2$. The two criteria may, however, be used only on condition that the scatter characterizing the reproducibility of the two methods compared is roughly the same.

Let us use the following application of the t-test as an example. Iron(III) is determined in iron(III) ammonium citrate by treating it with potassium iodide and titrating with thiosulphate solution the iodine liberated, using starch as indicator. It is sometimes recommended that the reaction mixture be let to stand for some time before titrating. The influence of this delay before titration on the accuracy of the results was investigated by a series of determinations A, in which titration was done immediately after mixing, and a series B in which the mixture was titrated after 30 minutes. The following results were obtained:

A	B
Fe^{3+}, %	Fe^{3+}, %
13.29	13.86
13.36	13.99
13.32	13.88
13.53	13.91
13.56	13.89
13.43	13.94
13.30	13.80
13.43	13.89
$\bar{x}_A = 13.402$	$\bar{x}_B = 13.895$
$s_A^2 = 0.0100$	$s_B^2 = 0.002857$

Because $n_A = n_B = 8$, Eq. 4.43 may be used: hence

$$t = \frac{0.493}{\sqrt{\dfrac{0.012857}{7}}} = 11.50$$

In Student's distribution tables we find $t = 2.145$ for $(1 - \alpha) = 0.95$: $\alpha = 0.05$ and $v = 2n - 2 = 14$. The calculated value $t = 11.50$ is substantially greater than the tabulated value, and the probability of the difference being caused by random errors only, is lower than 0.01: therefore the difference of the two means cannot be explained by random errors alone. The determinations of series A and B have been carried out under identical conditions, only the time between mixing and titration being different: therefore it is obvious that the delay before titration is of significance. This comparison only allows the statement that the results differ; it is impossible to decide which method is more accurate. To do this it would be necessary to know the true iron(III) content of the sample, i.e. the value μ. In the case given, however, it may be concluded that the solution should be allowed to stand for some time before titration, as it has been found that titrated solutions of series A liberate more iodine in the course of time, causing the blue colour of starch to be renewed.

This method of comparing the results obtained by use of two different methods has necessitated two series of parallel determinations of one sample. In practice, however, it happens more frequently that several different samples are analysed, each of them by the two methods to be compared. Obviously the number of determinations carried out by the two methods must be the same: let us denote it by n for each method (or for the number of samples analysed). Under these circumstances the two methods may be compared by calculating the criterion

$$t = (\bar{x}_A - \bar{x}_B)\sqrt{\frac{n(n - 1)}{\Sigma (D_i - D)^2}}. \tag{4.44}$$

where D_i is the positive or negative difference of the determinations carried out with the i-th sample by the two methods, and $\overline{D}$ is the mean difference. The calculation of the criterion may be simplified by means of a scheme similar to the following.

Sample	Method A	Method B	Difference D	$\mid D_i - \overline{D} \mid$	$(D_i - \overline{D})^2$
1	x_{1_A}	x_{1_B}	$D_1 = x_{1_A} - x_{1_B}$	$D_1 - \overline{D}$	$(D_1 - \overline{D})^2$
2	x_{2_A}	x_{2_B}	$D_2 = x_{2_A} - x_{2_B}$	$D_2 - \overline{D}$	$(D_2 - \overline{D})^2$
.	.	.	.	.	.
.	.	.	.	.	.
.	.	.	.	.	.
n	x_{n_A}	x_{n_B}	$D_n = x_{n_A} - x_{n_B}$	$D_n - \overline{D}$	$(D_n - \overline{D})^2$

$$\bar{x}_A = \frac{1}{n} \sum_{i=1}^{n} x_{iA}; \quad \bar{x}_B = \frac{1}{n} \sum_{i=1}^{n} x_{iB}; \quad \overline{D} = \frac{1}{n} \sum_{i=1}^{n} x_{iA} - x_{iB}; \quad \sum (D_i - \overline{D})^2$$

For an example of the calculation, let us use a comparison of the polarographic and complexometric determination of bismuth.

Sample	Bismuth, mg		D_i	$\mid D_i - \overline{D} \mid$	$(D_i - \overline{D})^2$
	Polaro-graphic	Complexo-metric			
1	40.4	40.0	0.4	0.225	0.050625
2	33.4	33.4	0.0	0.175	0.030625
3	35.7	35.5	0.2	0.025	0.000625
4	38.5	38.4	0.1	0.075	0.005625

$$\bar{x}_A = 37.00; \quad \bar{x}_B = 36.82; \quad \overline{D} = 0.175; \quad \Sigma(D_i - \overline{D})^2 = 0.087500$$

$$\bar{x}_A - \bar{x}_B = 0.18$$

$$t = 0.18 \sqrt{\frac{3 \times 4}{0.0875}} = 2.108.$$

Table 4.10 shows that the value found lies between the critical values for $(1 - \alpha) = 0.2$ and $(1 - \alpha) = 0.1$: thus it is clear that although the results of polarographic analysis are always higher, the difference may be explained by random errors.

Student's t-test is undoubtedly a very useful statistical test for the analyst, and its application is simple enough for anybody to be able to learn it quickly and surely. Since the criteria employed and the numbers of degrees of freedom differ somewhat from case to case, the individual criteria and the respective degrees of freedom are listed once more in Table 4.11.

In the section on estimates of the parameter σ, the estimate by use of the range was mentioned, and it was stated that its distribution differs from that of the estimate calculated from the sum of squares. It was also stated that the estimate from the range cannot replace the latter estimate in all cases. This also holds for testing by means of the t-test: in the relationship mentioned in Table 4.11 it is impossible to substitute for s values determined by means of $s_R = k_n \cdot R$. Since this estimate is very easily obtained,

Table 4.11. Review of the Different Characteristics of the t-Test

Application	Criterion	Number of degrees of freedom
Comparison of the mean $\bar{x}$ with the theoretical value:	$t = \dfrac{(\mu - \bar{x}) \cdot \sqrt{n}}{s}$	$n - 1$
Comparison of two means $\bar{x}_A; \bar{x}_B$	$t = \dfrac{\bar{x}_A - \bar{x}_B}{\sqrt{\dfrac{(n_A + n_B)(n_A s_A^2 + n_B s_B^2)}{n_A \cdot n_B(n_A + n_B - 2)}}}$	$(n_A + n_B - 2)$
(a) $n_A \neq n_B$ (b) $n_A = n_B = n$ (c) determination carried out with n samples, each sample being analysed by each of the two methods	$t = \dfrac{\bar{x}_A - \bar{x}_B}{\sqrt{\dfrac{s_A^2 + s_B^2}{n - 1}}}$	$2n - 2$
	$t = (\bar{x}_A - \bar{x}_B) \sqrt{\dfrac{n(n - 1)}{\Sigma(D_i - D)^2}}$	$n - 1$

and is specially suitable for small numbers of determinations, thus being well suited to practical analytical application, a test should also be mentioned which can be used for the same purpose but is based on the range. This is the so-called pseudo-t-test, also called Lord's u-test [75]. The test criterion is the relationship

$$u_0 = \frac{|\bar{x} - \mu|}{R} \tag{4.45}$$

or

$$u = \frac{|\bar{x}_1 - \bar{x}_2|}{R_1 + R_2} \tag{4.46}$$

The application of this test is quite similar to that of the t-test: the critical values are given in Table 4.12. Testing is either done for $n_1 - n_2 = n$ at a selected significance level or the probability of occurrence of the value u is determined by comparison with tabulated values for different confidence coefficients.

Table 4.12. Critical Values of Lord's Characteristic u_0 and u [75]

n	u_0		u	
	$\alpha = 0.05$	$\alpha = 0.01$	$\alpha = 0.05$	$\alpha = 0.01$
2	6.353	31.828	1.714	3.958
3	1.304	3.008	0.636	1.046
4	0.717	1.316	0.406	0.618
5	0.507	0.843	0.306	0.448
6	0.399	0.628	0.250	0.357
7	0.333	0.507	0.213	0.300
8	0.288	0.429	0.186	0.260
9	0.255	0.374	0.167	0.232
10	0.230	0.333	0.152	0.210

Let us describe another method of graphical testing by means of Lord's
u-test, which though only approximate, is extremely useful for current
practical work. It involves calculating the difference $\bar{x} - \mu$ or $\bar{x}_1 - \bar{x}_2$,
locating on the left-hand scale of the nomogram in Fig. 4.8 the value
corresponding to this difference, and connecting this with the value of R
or $R_1 + R_2$ on the oblique scale of the nomogram. The straight line
connecting the two points is now prolonged until it intersects the right-hand
scale of the nomogram on which values of u are plotted. The test criterion
value thus obtained is compared with the critical value in the right-hand
part of the graph for the given value of n; if the point thus obtained lies
above the curve, the difference is statistically highly significant: if it is

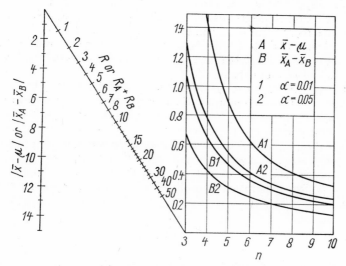

FIG. 4.8. Graph for comparison of the mean value with the expected value and of the
results of two different methods.

between the two curves, it is significant and if it is below the curve, it is
insignificant and may be explained by random errors only. An advantage
of this graphical test lies in the fact that it is possible to judge whether
a difference which is found to be insignificant for a small number of results,
might be proved to be significant if more determinations were to be carried
out. This is possible because if the point obtained is to the left of the curve,
then with a value of n greater than the value given, it would be above the
curve and be proved to be significant, so it is always worthwhile to carry
out another determination and repeat the test with a larger number of
results. A certain disadvantage of this test is the circumstance that it can
only be used if $\bar{x}_A$ and $\bar{x}_B$ are determined from the same number of
determinations, i.e. if $n_A = n_B$.

If the example of iodometric titration of ferric ions (see p. 112) were to be tested
with Lord's u-test, the difference would be $\bar{x}_A - \bar{x}_B = 0.493$ and the sum of ranges
$R_A + R_B = 0.46$. The value read from the graph is $u = 1.1$. This is obviously far greater
than the critical value plotted in the graph for $n = 8$ (actually the value $u = 1.1$ for $n = 8$

lies outside the graph). Therefore the difference cannot be explained by random errors alone, and it must be assumed that one of the methods employed does not give accurate results.

This graphical test, especially suitable for rapid orientation, is described by DOERFFEL [8].

4.16 The most suitable number of parallel determinations

We have already met with the problem of choosing the number of determinations: we have found that a large number of parallel determinations improves the precision and accuracy of results, and that with a large number of parallel determinations, accuracy is but little improved by carrying out more. This is illustrated in Fig. 4.3 (p. 95).

The problem now is to decide the minimum number of parallel determinations that is necessary to obtain a sufficiently reliable result, thus avoiding unnecessary work and expense.

In the case of physical measurements, especially if they are easy to repeat and it is thus unimportant whether five or even ten measurements more or less are done, it is quite easy to determine the number of parallel determinations necessary to achieve a result of predetermined accuracy. The calculation is carried out with the use of a relationship for the probability of a certain absolute magnitude of error $\Delta_{max} = |\bar{x} - \mu|$ not being exceeded. The value of z is found in the normal distribution tables (Table 4.7) for the selected probability α, and if σ is known, the equation

$$z = \frac{\Delta_{max}}{\sigma} \sqrt{n} \qquad (4.47)$$

is used to calculate the number of determinations

$$n = \frac{z^2 \cdot \sigma^2}{\Delta_{max}^2} \qquad (4.48)$$

or if σ is not known and must be replaced by the estimate s, n is calculated from the equation

$$n = \frac{t^2 \cdot s^2}{\Delta_{max}^2} \qquad (4.49)$$

Another method of determining the best number of parallel determinations has been proposed by BARANSKA [39]: the method is based on the equation $s_{\bar{x}} = s/\sqrt{n}$, which may also be written as:

$$\frac{\Delta_{s_{\bar{x}}}}{\Delta_n} = -\frac{s}{2\sqrt{n^3}} \qquad (4.50)$$

and for

$$\Delta_n = 1, \qquad \Delta_{s_{\bar{x}}} = -\frac{s}{2\sqrt{n^3}} \qquad \text{and} \qquad \frac{\Delta_{s_{\bar{x}}}}{s} = -\frac{1}{2\sqrt{n^3}}.$$

When $\Delta_{s_{\bar{x}}}$, the relative error of the standard deviation of the mean, is expressed in per cent, we obtain

$$\frac{\Delta_{s_{\bar{x}}}}{\Delta_s} = -\frac{50}{\sqrt{n^3}} \quad \text{and} \quad n = \sqrt[3]{\frac{2500\,s^2}{\Delta_{s_{\bar{x}}}^2}}.$$

Selecting a certain demand for the value of $\Delta_{s_{\bar{x}}}$, we may determine the number of analyses needed, n. E.g. for $\Delta_{s_{\bar{x}}} = 50\,\%$, $n = 1$, for $\Delta_{s_{\bar{x}}} = 10\,\%$ we get $n = 3$ and for $\Delta_{s_{\bar{x}}} = 1\,\%$, $n = 14$ etc.

All these relationships could also be applied to the determination of the number of parallel chemical analyses; however, the value of n is in principle determined by the preselected absolute error Δ_{max} or the ratio of the standard deviation of the mean value to the standard deviation of the individual determination Δ_s, so that the practical significance of this calculation is questionable.

Of greater utility is a consideration in which no a priori demands are made, since these involve a certain degree of subjective influence. The relationship

$$\Delta = \frac{t \cdot s}{\sqrt{n}} \tag{4.51}$$

is used to study the variation of the absolute error Δ with the number of determinations n: such a number of determinations is then carried out, that the value of Δ will be decreased by a substantial amount. The value of s may be obtained from a special set of test analyses, or by assessment of repeated analyses of several practical samples. It should be mentioned, however, that this procedure is not quite exact from the statistical aspect: a value of σ estimated from a larger number of different analyses is being applied to analyses which may have been carried out with a different sample, etc.

Now let us carry out a statistical analysis, the purpose of which will be the determination of a useful number of parallel determinations of nitrogen by the Kjeldahl method, using values of s given in the first example in section 4.8:

N, %	s
1	0.0320
3	0.0505
5	0.0549
15	0.0762

Obviously the value of s rises with rising nitrogen content, and thus it is probable that the confidence interval will also differ for the results of analyses of samples of different nitrogen concentration.

Let us first carry out the calculation for a content of $1\,\%\,N$ ($s = 0.0320$)

Number of determinations	$\Delta = \dfrac{t \cdot s}{\sqrt{n}}$	$L = \dfrac{100\Delta}{x}\%$	Difference
2	$12.7 \times 0.71 \times 0.032 = 0.289$	28.90%	
3	$4.3 \times 0.58 \times 0.032 = 0.0798$	7.98%	20.92
4	$3.2 \times 0.50 \times 0.032 = 0.0512$	5.12%	2.86
5	$2.8 \times 0.45 \times 0.032 = 0.0403$	4.03%	1.09
6	$2.6 \times 0.41 \times 0.032 = 0.0341$	3.41%	0.62

For 15 % N ($s = 0.076$):

Number of deformations	$\Delta = \dfrac{t \cdot s}{\sqrt{n}}$	$L = \dfrac{100\Delta}{x}\%$	Difference
2	$12.7 \times 0.71 \times 0.076 = 0.685$	4.56%	3.30
3	$4.3 \times 0.58 \times 0.076 = 0.189$	1.26%	0.45
4	$3.2 \times 0.50 \times 0.076 = 0.121$	0.81%	0.17
5	$2.8 \times 0.45 \times 0.076 = 0.096$	0.64%	0.10
6	$2.6 \times 0.41 \times 0.076 = 0.081$	0.54%	

When 1 % of N is being determined, the third determination improves the reliability of the result to a substantial extent: the effect of more determinations is far less. Therefore it will be of advantage to carry out three parallel determinations. In the determination of 15 % of N the relative confidence interval is already rather narrow for $n = 2$: a third parallel determination narrows this interval, but the effect achieved is hardly proportionate to the work and time expended on the analysis.

Very similar considerations may be applied to all analytical methods. The necessary number of determinations cannot, however, be determined in a general way with absolute validity: such calculations can only serve as guides, and the number of parallel determinations to be carried out depends on the requirements of the result as well as on the precision of the method and composition of the sample. Obviously the minimum number of determinations is $n = 2$, since the redundance of a single result is zero. With two parallel determinations the confidence interval is generally rather wide, but in practical applications, two is the most frequent number of determinations. A third analysis usually improves the reliability of the results to a substantial degree, and moreover, as will be shown later, with three results it is already possible to find and eliminate a result subject to a gross error, even if the permitted difference of the determinations is unknown. Three parallel determinations therefore are used mainly in those cases where results of inferior reproducibility are obtained or if the analysis is very important. Four determinations should be considered only with very important analyses which either are easily carried out or are poorly reproducible, e.g. distillation methods. In all cases where the determination can be repeated easily, e.g. if a sufficient volume of stock solution is available for aliquots for titration etc, it is preferable to carry out a larger number of parallel determination: when starting from different weighed samples, the most frequent number is $n = 2$ or 3. The decision of how many parallel analyses are to be carried out may be influenced by other aspects besides the reliability of the results. Let us mention just as a point of interest, that SHEWELL [87] for example determines the number of parallel determinations by means of a relationship which involves the standard deviation and costs of performing the analysis proper, the calculated number of determinations being lower if the determination is either sufficiently precise or too expensive.

4.17 Comparison of the precision of two methods by means of the F-test

We have learned in the section on the use of the t-test how to compare the results of analyses characterized by the mean values. In practice, however, it is also frequently necessary to decide which of two methods will lead to results of better reproducibility.

If the precise value of the scatter σ^2 were known, it would obviously be possible to consider the method having lower scatter as being the more reproducible. Practically, however, only the estimates s^2 are known, with a limited degree of reliability. Thus a case may occur in which the estimates of the same σ value will differ somewhat. The scatter estimates of the analytical results, which have Gaussian distribution, are therefore compared by means of the SNEDECOR criterion [6, 7, 8, 12, 14, 23, 24, 25]

$$F = \frac{s_A^2}{s_B^2} \qquad (4.52)$$

Table 4.13. The Snedecor *F*-Distribution

Critical values are given for $(1 - \alpha) = 0.95$ in the upper lines and for $(1 - \alpha) = 0.90$ in the lower lines.

ν_2 \ ν_1	1	2	3	4	5	6	8	10	12	14
1	161	200	216	225	230	234	239	242	244	245
	4052	4999	5403	5625	5764	5859	5981	6056	6103	6142
2	18.51	19.00	19.16	19.25	19.30	19.33	19.37	19.39	19.41	19.42
	98.49	99.00	99.17	99.25	99.30	99.33	99.36	99.40	99.42	99.43
3	10.13	8.55	9.28	9.12	9.01	8.94	8.84	8.78	8.74	8.71
	34.12	30.82	29.46	28.71	28.24	27.91	27.49	27.23	27.05	26.92
4	7.71	6.94	6.59	6.39	6.26	6.16	6.04	5.96	5.91	5.87
	21.20	18.20	16.69	15.98	15.52	15.21	14,80	14,54	14.37	14.24
5	6.61	5.79	5.41	5.19	5.05	4.95	4.82	4.74	4.68	4.64
	16.26	13.27	12.06	11.39	10.97	10.67	10.27	10.05	9.89	9.77
6	5.99	5.14	4.76	4.53	4.39	4.28	4.15	4.06	4.00	3.96
	13.74	10.92	9.78	9.15	8.75	8.47	8.10	7.87	7.72	7.60
7	5.59	4.74	4.35	4.12	3.97	3.87	3.73	3.63	3.57	3.52
	12.25	9.55	8.45	7.85	7.46	7.19	6.84	6.62	6.47	6.35
8	5.32	4.46	4.07	3.84	3.69	3.58	3.44	3.34	3.28	3.23
	11.26	8.65	7.59	7.01	6.63	6.73	6.03	5.82	5.67	5.56
9	5.12	4.26	3.86	3.63	3.48	3.37	3.23	3.13	3.07	3.02
	10.56	8.02	6.99	6.42	6.06	5.80	5.47	5.26	5.11	5.00
10	4.96	4.10	3.71	3.48	3.33	3.22	3.07	2.97	2.91	2.86
	10.04	7.56	6.55	5.99	5.64	5.39	5.06	4.85	4.71	4.60
12	4.75	3.88	3.49	3.26	3.11	3.00	2.85	2.76	2.69	2.64
	9.33	6.93	5.95	5.41	5.06	4.82	4.50	4.30	4.16	4.05
17	4.45	3.59	3.20	2.96	2.81	2.70	2.55	2.45	2.38	2.33
	8.40	6.11	5.18	4.67	4.34	4.10	3.80	3.60	3.45	3.35

which again has a certain probability distribution. This distribution will not be described here in detail: it suffices to say that it is asymmetric, depends on two degrees of freedom and is defined for positive values of F only. The degrees of freedom are two parameters which depend on the number of determinations carried out for the calculation of the individual estimates s_A^2, s_B^2. Critical values of F are given in Table 4.13 for $(1 - \alpha) = 0.95$ and $(1 - \alpha) = 0.90$. The two estimates are compared by substitution in Eq. 4.52 in such a way that the larger value of s^2 is put in the numerator and the calculated value of F is compared with the tabulated value for a number of degrees of freedom $v_A = (n_A - 1)$ and $v_B = (n_B - 1)$, n_A, n_B being the numbers of determinations carried out for the calculation of s_A^2, s_B^2. If the calculated value is lower than the tabulated one, the scatter values differ only within the limits of random error: if it is greater, the method with the lower scatter gives definitely superior results. If we were to compare the reproducibility of two methods on the basis of pairs of parallel determinations carried out with a series of samples, it would be of more advantage to calculate the values of F from the relationship [42]

$$F = \frac{R_A^2}{R_B^2} \cdot \frac{m_B}{m_A} \qquad (4.53)$$

where R_A, R_B are the ranges of determinations carried out by the methods A, B and m_A, m_B are numbers of pairs of determinations, i.e. the number of samples analysed by means of the methods A, B: $v_A = m_A$ and $v_B = m_B$.

In practical analytical chemistry, the F-test is used only rarely: the reason is that accuracy is of more interest than the precision of results. On the other hand, the F-test finds a suitable field of application in so-called *analysis of variance* ("ANOVA") which is the basic principle of studying the significance of influences participating in the origin of the final error of a chemical analysis. This problem will be taken up in the following section.

4.18 Determining the influence on the final result, of errors of individual operations

In any analysis which is complicated to some degree, the errors of all operations carried out in the procedure participate in creating the error of the final result, the influence of the individual errors being different. If it is required to improve the result by modifying the experimental conditions, it is best to try to eliminate that source of error which contributes most to the final error.

In Chapter 3 we have seen the causes of different errors occurring during an analytical procedure. It is true that we are able to explain the origin of such errors and sometimes even to determine the probable magnitude of errors occurring in the individual operations, but these considerations can hardly help us to find out which of the operations is the source of the most serious error. This may be clarified by experimental analysis of the scatter of results, arranged in such a way that the influence of one specific operation prevails in the scatter. If the variance of results obtained is significantly greater than the overall variance, this specific operation may be regarded as the source of the gravest error, and attempts may then be made to modify this operation in some way, or to eliminate it totally from the procedure, or replace it by a different and more suitable one. This type of elucidation of errors caused by individual operations of the analytical procedure is described in a manner easy to understand, by SHEWELL [87], MAURICE [78] and NALIMOV [25].

Let us now describe the procedure by means of a definite example. The determination of nitrogen in an organic substance by the Kjeldahl method involves the following operations:

sample weighing
mineralization
distillation
titration.

The first and last operations *(weighing and titration)* are, in fact, measurements. The sum of errors of the two measurements (i.e. even though we disregard the fact that errors may possibly compensate each other) is lower than the final error of the final determination. This means that the error of the final result includes errors which originate in *mineralization* of the sample and in the ammonia *distillation*. When we wish to find out which is the source of the larger error, we must carry out several determinations in such a manner as to make the influence of mineralization prevail in their scatter, and others in which the influence of distillation will prevail. With a suitable arrangement of the experiments it is possible to express these influences numerically. Let us arrange the determination in this way:

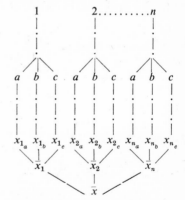

The variance of results obtained from different aliquots of one mineralized sample (x_{1a}, x_{1b}, x_{1c}) will then be a measure of errors caused by distillation, because all the results have one mineralization in common, while the variance of the means $\bar{x}_1$, $\bar{x}_2$ etc around the overall mean $\bar{x}$ is mainly due to mineralization, because calculations of the mean $\bar{x}_i$ will, to a large degree, eliminate the variability and imprecision of the results caused by the individual distillations. This procedure may be illustrated with the example of 18 results of Kjeldahl nitrogen determinations in acetanilide (theoretical value 10.36 % N), as given in Table 4.14, and the same number of nitrogen determinations in ferron (7-iodo-8-hydroxy-quinoline-5-sulphonic acid, theoretical value 3.98 % N), Table 4.15.

Three parallel determinations have been carried out from each of six sample weights of roughly the same magnitude.

It follows from Table 4.14 that neither σ_K^2 nor σ_D^2 differs substantially from σ^2 nor do they differ from each other, although the exact agreement of $\sigma_K^2 = \sigma_D^2$ is largely accidental. This means that when nitrogen is being determined by the Kjeldahl method

Table 4.14. Determination of Nitrogen in Acetanilide

Sample i	Result $x_{i,j}$	Mean $\bar{x}_i$	$\Delta_i x_{i,j} =$ $= \lvert x_{i,j} - \bar{x}_i \rvert$	$\Delta_i^2 x_{i,j}$	$\Delta x_{i,j} =$ $= \lvert x_{i,j} - \bar{x} \rvert$	$\Delta^2 x_{i,j}$	$\Delta \bar{x}_i =$ $= \lvert \bar{x}_i - \bar{x} \rvert$	$\Delta^2 \bar{x}$
1	10.22	10.32	0.10	0.0100	0.10	0.0100	0.00	0.0000
	10.35		0.03	0.0009	0.03	0.0009		
	10.38		0.06	0.0036	0.06	0.0036		
2	10.28	10.33	0.05	0.0025	0.04	0.0016	0.01	0.0001
	10.36		0.03	0.0009	0.04	0.0016		
	10.36		0.03	0.0009	0.04	0.0016		
3	10.14	10.19	0.05	0.0025	0.18	0.0324	0.13	0.0169
	10.14		0.05	0.0025	0.18	0.0324		
	10.28		0.09	0.0081	0.04	0.0016		
4	10.23	10.32	0.09	0.0081	0.09	0.0081	0.00	0.000C
	10.30		0.02	0.0004	0.02	0.0004		
	10.43		0.11	0.0121	0.11	0.0121		
5	10.33	10.39	0.06	0.0036	0.01	0.0001	0.07	0.0049
	10.36		0.03	0.0009	0.04	0.0016		
	10.44		0.05	0.0025	0.12	0.0144		
6	10.35	10.38	0.03	0.0009	0.03	0.0009	0.06	0.0036
	10.38		0.00	0.0000	0.06	0.0036		
	10.41		0.03	0.0009	0.09	0.0081		

$$x = 10.32 \qquad \Sigma\Delta_i^2 x_{i,j} = 0.0613 \qquad \Sigma\Delta^2 x_{i,j} = 0.1350 \qquad \Sigma\Delta^2 \bar{x}_i = 0.0255$$

mineralization scatter $\quad \sigma_K^2 = \dfrac{\Sigma\Delta^2\bar{x}_i}{6-1} = \dfrac{0.0255}{5} = 0.0051$

distillation scatter $\quad \sigma_D^2 = \dfrac{\Sigma\Delta_i^2 x_{i,j}}{18-6} = \dfrac{0.0613}{12} = 0.0051$

overall scatter $\quad \sigma^2 = \dfrac{\Sigma\Delta^2 x_{i,j}}{18-1} = \dfrac{0.1350}{17} = 0.0079$

value from use of F-test $\quad F_1 = \dfrac{\sigma^2}{\sigma_K^2} = \dfrac{0.0079}{0.0051} = 1.55$

$$F_2 = \dfrac{\sigma_2}{\sigma_K^2} = \dfrac{0.0079}{0.0051} = 1.55$$

$$F_3 = \dfrac{\sigma^2 D}{\sigma_D^2} = 1.00$$

Critical values found in Table 4.13

$$F(17,5) \ = 4.6$$
$$F(17,12) = 2.6$$

in a substance as easy to mineralize as acetanilide, mineralization and distillation participate to roughly the same extent as sources of variability of the results.

The situation is somewhat different with substances which are difficult to mineralize. It is seen from Table 4.15 that in ferron analyses there is a significant difference between overall scatter and scatter of the distillation operation, overall scatter being significantly greater. There is also a difference between the scatter of mineralization and distillation,

Table 4.15. Determination of Nitrogen in Ferron

Sample i	Result $x_{i,j}$	Mean $\bar{x}_i$	$\Delta_i x_{i,j} =$ $= \lvert x_{i,j} - \bar{x}_i \rvert$	$\Delta_i^2 x_{i,j}$	$\Delta x_{i,j} =$ $= \lvert x_{i,j} - \bar{x} \rvert$	$\Delta^2 x_{i,j}$	$\Delta x_i =$ $= \lvert \bar{x}_i - \bar{x} \rvert$	$\Delta^2 \bar{x}_i$
1	1.79	1.77	0.02	0.0004	0.14	0.0196	0.16	0.0256
	1.75		0.02	0.0004	0.18	0.0324		
	1.77		0.00	0.0000	0.16	0.0256		
2	0.82	0.88	0.06	0.0036	1.11	1.2321	1.05	1.1025
	0.92		0.04	0.0016	1.01	1.0201		
	0.90		0.02	0.0004	1.03	1.0609		
3	1.57	1.58	0.01	0.0001	0.36	0.1296	0.35	0.1225
	1.61		0.03	0.0009	0.32	0.1024		
	1.58		0.00	0.0000	0.35	0.1225		
4	2.01	2.02	0.01	0.0001	0.08	0.0064	0.09	0.0081
	1.98		0.04	0.0016	0.05	0.0025		
	2.08		0.06	0.0036	0.15	0.0225		
5	3.16	3.19	0.03	0.0009	1.23	1.5129	1.26	1.5876
	3.21		0.02	0.0004	1.27	1.6129		
	3.21		0.02	0.0004	1.27	1.6129		
6	2.12	2.16	0.04	0.0016	0.19	0.0361	0.23	0.0529
	2.21		0.05	0.0025	0.28	0.0784		
	2.17		0.01	0.0001	0.24	0.0576		

$$x = 1.93 \qquad \Sigma \Delta_i^2 x_{i,j} = 0.0186 \qquad \Sigma \Delta^2 x_{i,j} = 8.6874 \qquad \Sigma \Delta^2 \bar{x}_i = 2.8992$$

mineralization scatter $\quad \sigma_K^2 = \dfrac{\Sigma \Delta^2 \bar{x}_i}{6-1} = \dfrac{2.8992}{5} = 0.5798$

distillation scatter $\quad \sigma_D^2 = \dfrac{\Sigma \Delta_i^2 x_{i,j}}{18-6} = \dfrac{0.0186}{12} = 0.0015$

overall scatter $\quad \sigma^2 = \dfrac{\Sigma \Delta^2 x_{i,j}}{18-1} = \dfrac{8.6874}{17} = 0.5110$

values from use of F-test $\quad F_1 = \dfrac{\sigma_K^2}{2} = \dfrac{0.5798}{0.5110} = 1.13$

$$F_2 = \dfrac{\sigma^2}{\sigma_D^2} = \dfrac{0.5110}{0.0015} = 340.6$$

$$F_3 = \dfrac{\sigma_K^2}{\sigma_D^2} = \dfrac{0.5798}{0.0015} = 386.5$$

critical F values found in Table 4.13

$$F(17,5) = 4.6$$
$$F(17,12) = 2.6$$

mineralization scatter being significantly greater. This means that mineralization causes most of the variability of the final results, rather than distillation, which causes only slight scatter. The absolute values of the results are also remarkable: 1.77, 0.88, 1.58, 2.02, 3.19 and 2.16 % N, found in a substance containing theoretically 3.98 % N, although a certain difference from the theoretical value need not mean an analytical error, as the sample was taken from an industrial production batch of ferron, not from a pure standard substance. It is to be seen from the scatter analysis that conventional Kjeldahl treatment does not cause complete mineralization of the substance. Actually, modification of the Kjeldahl process (prolonged duration, selenium catalyst) allowed the error to be eliminated, and the results then obtained agreed with the theoretical nitrogen content, the values found being 3.92 and 3.95 % N.

4.19 Gross errors and the elimination of outlying results

Gross errors are those isolated errors, the magnitude of which identifies them at first sight as errors far exceeding random errors in size. It must be kept in mind, however, that according to the Gaussian law of random error distribution it is, strictly speaking, impossible to regard even the largest errors as non-random although the probability of occurrence of a very great random error is slight, i.e. such a large error will occur only very occasionally in a large number of analyses. True gross errors, however, occurring e.g. as a consequence of mistakes, may occur at any time, and their occurrence cannot very well be explained by the validity of the normal error distribution law, but rather as a deviation from this law.

Causes of gross errors are generally large deviations from the correct procedure of analysis, mostly caused by the analyst himself. The occurrence of a gross error, even in only one of several parallel determinations, may be a grave danger to the accuracy of the final result. Gross errors differ from systematic ones, which also distort the final result, mainly in magnitude, irregularity and isolation of occurrence. In practice use is made of the fact that an analytical result subject to a gross error differs greatly from the other results. For this reason such results are sometimes called outlying results, and they are not taken into account in the calculation of the mean, or the analysis is repeated. The elimination of outlying results is in principle based on the difference between the suspicious result and the other results or their mean: the same point of view is used in statistical methods of deciding whether given results are distorted by gross errors: in contrast to the elimination of gross errors purely from experience, such criteria are quite objective.

The literature includes quite a number of criteria for the elimination of outlying results, but the majority of these are based on knowing the value of the standard deviation σ, which of course cannot be expected in practical analytical work. Other criteria used to eliminate outlying results of analyses demand an estimate of the standard deviation which, obviously, must be obtained from a series of parallel determinations differing from the series containing the suspected gross error: this follows from the fact that the standard deviation must be independent of the outlying result which is to be eliminated. It is clear again that for practical work this calculation of the standard deviation from a different series of determinations is disadvantageous, since in general it is impossible or inconvenient to carry out another series of parallel analyses. Therefore these criteria will not be discussed.

Recently, some criteria have been derived for the elimination of outlying results, which do not necessitate a preliminary knowledge of the standard deviation σ, nor its calculation from another series of parallel determinations.

The following relationship has been proposed for eliminating outlying results:

$$T_n = \frac{x_n - \bar{x}}{s_\lambda} \quad \text{or} \quad T_1 = \frac{\bar{x} - x_1}{s_1} \quad (4.54)$$

s_1 being calculated from the analytical results by means of Eq. 4.12, (p. 86), $s_1 = \sqrt{\dfrac{\Sigma \Delta^2}{n}}$. The value of x_n or x_1 in Eq. 4.54 denotes the highest or lowest analytical result, i.e. the value of the criterion T_n or T_1 will always be positive. The calculated values of T_n or T_1 are then compared with tabulated critical values of $T(n, \alpha)$, for the selected value of $(1 - \alpha)$ and the number of determinations n, from Table 4.16. The result x_n or x_1 is eliminated if T_n or $T_1 > T(n, \alpha)$.

Since the use of the criterion in Eq. 4.54 involves calculating the standard deviation s_2, DEAN and DIXON have derived another criterion [46]

$$Q_n = \frac{x_n - x_{n-1}}{R} \quad \text{or} \quad Q_1 = \frac{x_2 - x_1}{R} \quad (4.55)$$

where $R = x_n - x_1$, and the analytical results are arranged again in the order $x_1 \leqq x_2 \leqq x_3 \ldots \leqq x_n$. The criterion Q_n or Q_1 is obviously used in dependence on whether the value of a certain determination is suspected of being either too high or too low. The criterion Q_n or Q_1 is calculated and compared with the critical values of $Q(n, \alpha)$ from Table 4.17 for the respective values of $(1 - \alpha)$ and n, in order to decide whether the result of the analysis represents a gross error [i.e. when Q_n or $Q_1 > Q(n, \alpha)$].

The two tests mentioned may be used to eliminate deviations of the results even if the number of parallel determinations is small: however,

Table 4.16. Critical Values of $T(n, \alpha)$ for Eliminating Gross Errors

n \ α	0.01	0.025	0.05	0.10
3	1.414	1.414	1.412	1.406
4	1.723	1.710	1.689	1.645
5	1.955	1.917	1.869	1.791
6	2.130	2.067	1.996	1.894
7	2.265	2.182	2.093	1.974
8	2.374	2.273	2.172	2.041
9	2.464	2.349	2.237	2.097
10	2.540	2.414	2.294	2.146
11	2.606	2.470	2.343	2.190
12	2.663	2.519	2.387	2.229
13	2.714	2.562	2.426	2.264
14	2.759	2.602	2.461	2.297
15	2.800	2.638	2.493	2.326
16	2.837	2.670	2.523	2.354
17	2.871	2.701	2.551	2.380
18	2.903	2.728	2.577	2.404
19	2.932	2.754	2.600	2.426
20	2.959	2.778	2.623	2.447

it is never possible to eliminate a gross error from only two determinations, because it is never possible to decide which of the two results is subject to a gross error. The criterion T is based on the standard deviation and will therefore be useful for larger numbers of parallel determinations, while the criterion Q, based on the range, is suitable for low values of n. Moreover, critical Q-values are tabulated in Table 4.17 for values of $n \leq 7$ only.

Table 4.17. Critical Values of $Q(n, \alpha)$ for the Elimination of Gross Errors

n \ α	0.10	0.05	0.02	0.01
3	0.886	0.941	0.972	0.988
4	0.679	0.765	0.846	0.889
5	0.557	0.642	0.729	0.760
6	0.482	0.560	0.644	0.698
7	0.434	0.507	0.586	0.637

The use of the two criteria for eliminating an outlying result may be illustrated by the following example.

Five parallel determinations of zinc in an organic substance have been carried out. Since it is suspected that the largest value involves a gross error, this assumption is tested by means of the Q and T-tests. The analytical results are arranged in order of magnitude:

$$x_i = \% \, Zn$$

16.84	$\bar{x} = 17.03$
16.86	$\tilde{x} = 16.91$
16.91	
16.93	$s_2 = \sqrt{\dfrac{\Sigma \Delta^2}{n}} = 0.292$
17.61	

Using the criterion T to test for the presence of a gross error, we obtain

$$T_5 = \frac{17.61 - 17.03}{0.292} = 1.99$$

Since for $\alpha = 0.05$ and $n = 5$, Table 4.16 shows $T(5, 0.05) = 1.869 < T_5 = 1.99$, the largest result must be eliminated.

Using the criterion Q we obtain

$$Q_5 = \frac{17.61 - 16.93}{17.61 - 16.84} = 0.883$$

From Table 4.17 we obtain $Q(5, 0.05) = 0.642$. Thus, again, $Q_5 > Q(5, 0.05)$ and the suspect result must be eliminated according to this criterion too.

After eliminating the value of $Zn = 17.61\%$ we calculate the following data:

$$\bar{x} = 16.885$$
$$\tilde{x} = 16.885 \qquad s_2 = \sqrt{\frac{\Sigma \Delta^2}{n}} = 0.0364$$

Note that before the outlying result was eliminated, there was a great difference between the mean and the median $\bar{x} - \tilde{x} = 0.12$, and four of the five deviations from the mean had negative signs. The confidence interval for all the five results may be determined with the use of the value $s = 0.292$ (we are concerned with the precision of determinations, carried out with a specific sample and under specific conditions) and of the t-distribution for $\nu = 5 - 1 = 4$ and $(1 - \alpha) = 0.95$. This gives the limits of the confidence interval as $L_1 = 16.66\%$ and $L_2 = 17.39\%$. If the highest value, $17.61\% \, Zn$ is eliminated, $\bar{x}$ becomes equal to $\tilde{x}$ and the number of deviations of positive and negative signs lower; i.e. $v = 4 - 1 = 3$ and a larger value of t must be used to calculate the confidence interval; the confidence interval is narrowed to $L_1 = 16.83\%$ and $L_2 = 16.94\%$, because the standard deviation has decreased from 0.292 to 0.0364. This means that when the outlying value has been eliminated, the final result has become more reliable.

In concluding, let us mention that elimination of outlying results by means of the Q-test can also be done with the use of the graph in Fig. 4.9. The difference $x_1 - x_2$ or $x_n - x_{n-1}$ on the left-hand scale is joined with the value of R on the oblique scale, and the connecting line is prolonged to the right-hand scale, where the intersection gives the value of Q. This value is then compared with the critical value for the given value of n in the right-hand part of the graph. This graphical test is also described by DOERFFEL [8].

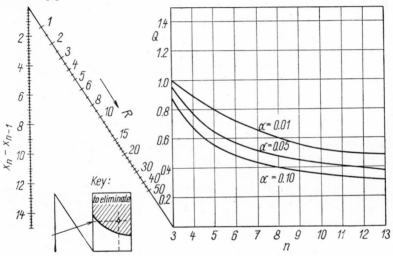

FIG. 4.9. Graph for elimination of outlying result.

4.20 The permitted difference of two parallel determinations

When two parallel determinations have been carried out, which is the most frequent case in practical analytical chemistry, none of the results can be excluded as it is not known which of the two involves a gross error. Assuming that the standard deviation is known, the permitted difference between two parallel determinations may be determined by means of an approximate but very simple relationship

$$R_{max} = a \cdot \sigma \tag{4.56}$$

the coefficient a being found in Table 4.18. Since, in practice, the parameter σ is frequently unknown and must be estimated from the mean range by means of Eq. 4.17 (p. 88), i.e. for $n = 2$ by means of the relation $s = 0.886R$ (see Table 4.4, p. 89), Table 4.18 also includes values of $b = k_n \cdot a$ for the selected value of $(1 - \alpha)$, and we may write immediately

$$R_{max} = b \cdot \bar{R} \tag{4.57}$$

This relationship is more important in practical analysis than would appear at first sight. If, in routine analytical control, pairs of determinations are always done, it is very easy to determine their permitted difference by calculating the absolute value of the difference of the two determinations R_i and the mean of these differences $\bar{R} = \dfrac{1}{m} \Sigma R_i$ (m being the number of samples analysed), for rather a large number (e.g. 25 or more) of such pairs of determinations, carried out with different samples of roughly the same composition.

Table 4.18. Values of the Coefficients a and b
for Calculating the Permitted Difference of Different
Numbers of Parallel Determinations n

	a			b		
$\alpha =$	0.10	0.05	0.01	0.10	0.05	0.01
$n = 2$	2.33	2.77	3.64	2.06	2.46	3.23
3	2.90	3.31	4.12	1.71	1.96	2.43
4	3.24	3.63	4.40	1.57	1.76	2.14
5	3.48	3.86	4.60	1.50	1.66	1.98

Multiplication of the mean difference by the tabulated value of b immediately gives the permitted difference of the determinations.

As an example, let us determine the permitted difference of a Kjeldahl nitrogen determination on samples with a content of roughly 3% N, with $\bar{R} = 0.057$. For $\alpha = 0.05$ we then obtain $R_{\max} = 2.46 \times 0.057 = 0.14\%$. Two parallel determinations gave results of 2.96% and 3.19% N: the difference $3.19 - 2.96 = 0.23\%$ is greater than $R_{\max}$, i.e. one of the determinations may involve a gross error. A third determination resulted in 2.92% N, i.e. $x = \dfrac{2.92 + 2.96}{2} = 2.94\%$ N and the value of 3.19% must be eliminated, because it is too high.

Finally, a few words about the problem of determining the gross error of one of two determinations: as already stated, a large difference between the two determinations signifies the presence of a gross error in one of the two results: however, it is not known which of the two this is. This can be decided only by means of a third determination: the mean is then calculated from those two results which agree better mutually. This procedure is well known to every analyst, even though he is not familiar with statistical methods: a calculation of the permitted difference will only aid the analyst in deciding on the size of difference which may be accepted as permissible. However, this method is not suitable for determining the permitted difference between the results of two laboratories, e.g. the supplier's and the consumer's laboratory. The difference between results obtained in different laboratories may be tested, for example, by means of the t-test or u-test (see section 4.15).

One other important point should be kept in mind. It has been stated already that reproducibility is, to a certain degree, a criterion of the accuracy of results: this, however, does not mean that results of outstanding reliability can be obtained by choosing a very small permitted difference of parallel determinations (e.g. less than a value corresponding to the objective value of R_{max}) and repeating the analysis until two results fit into the chosen limits. Such a procedure is a deliberate distortion of the random character of selection of results for the calculation of the mean, and might rather cause some degree of distortion of the final results. The only way of improving the accuracy of results is experimental elucidation of the causes of their inferior reproducibility, followed by a modification of the analytical procedure designed so as to achieve more precise results: then, of course, the accuracy of the results will improve, unless the procedure involves a systematic error. After all, any improvement of the results of analysis is possible solely by means of an experimental search for a better and more accurate procedure.

4.21 The limit of detection

In trace analysis there is, besides precision and accuracy, another important criterion of analytical methods — the so-called *detection limit*, i.e. the smallest amount of the component to be determined, which still is large enough to be detected. This value is usually expressed either in absolute units, i.e. weight amounts of the component determined, or in relative units, i.e. the concentration of the component (in ppm etc). Individual authors define the detection limit in different ways, and there are frequent discussions of the practical suitability of the individual definitions. All however agree that the detection limit must be defined in statistical terms as the least value which can be distinguished from zero. For example GOTTSCHALK [12] defines the detection limit as the least amount which may be distinguished from zero, and assumes it to be invariable and constant. The detection limit is thus given by the relationship

$$\underline{x} = t \cdot s \tag{4.58}$$

KAISER [69, 70] defines this quantity in the same manner, but he does not assume "zero" to be an invariable constant. Instead Kaiser considers the variability, or "*noise*", of the zero value. His definition of the detection limit is expressed by the relationship

$$\underline{x} = \bar{x}_0 + k \cdot s_0 \tag{4.59}$$

where $\underline{x}$ is the smallest measurable value, $\bar{x}_0$ is the mean value of the zero or of the blank experiment, s_0 is the standard deviation characterizing the variability of this zero or of the blank experiment, and the value of the factor k may be obtained from tables of the Gaussian distribution. Some values of k and the respective probabilities are given in Table 4.19.

Table 4.19. Values of the Factor k and their Probabilities

k	Probability, %
3	99.86
2	97.73

Kaiser recommends $k = 3$, and the same value is also used by DOERFFEL [8]. These authors thus try, by means of using a k value corresponding to rather a high probability, to virtually eliminate errors of the first kind, i.e. errors which originate by a random variation of noise being mistaken for an analytical signal. ROOS [85] also takes errors of the second kind into account, i.e. an error caused by an element, present in an amount higher than the detection limit, not being found: he therefore recommends a lower value of k, e.g. 2. The same value is used by WILSON [98]. According to this criterion it seems that the detection limit will only be influenced by the variability of the blank experiment, i.e. "*zero noise*", and not by its absolute value. We know however from practical experience that the absolute value of the blank experiment is a factor limiting the detection limit. SVOBODA and GERBATSCH [95] set out from the results of statistical signal detection to attempt to avoid errors of the first as well as the second kind. Conditions in such a manner as to make the mean risk minimum are selected. There is a certain difference between "zero noise" i.e. variability of measurement of the zero position, having a normal distribution (so-called "white zero noise") and characterized by the value σ_M, and the variability of the blank experiment, which is given by the noise and variability of the determination proper of a small but non-zero concentration of substance in the blank experiment. This variability has a lognormal distribution and is characterized by σ_{Bl}. The overall variability of determination of the blank experiment is thus expressed, according to Table 4.6 (p. 94) by the equation

$$\sigma_0 = \sqrt{\sigma_M^2 + \sigma_{Bl}^2} \qquad (4.60)$$

and is always greater than the zero noise, and very frequently directly proportional to the absolute value of the blank experiment. This work has been continued by ECKSCHLAGER [54], who has shown the extent to which the absolute value of the blank experiment influences the reliability of trace analyses and the manner which it elevates the detection limit. WINEFORDNER and co-workers [99] define the detection limit as the least signal which may be distinguished from the zero noise by means of Students' t-test. This detection limit is not constant; it depends e.g. on the number of parallel determinations carried out.

In concluding this section it should also be mentioned that the problem of the detection limit is not yet fully solved and continues to be discussed by different authors. The notation and terminology are also not yet unified.

4.22 Non-parametric methods

All statistical methods described so far in this text are based on the assumption that the distribution of results of parallel determinations is controlled by a certain mathematical model, e.g. that it is normal: these methods are always used on the basis of the theory of probability, and always include the estimate of some parameter: in the t-test estimates of the param ers μ and σ: in the F-test estimates of σ^2, etc. Such are called *parametric methods*. However, if the probability distribution of the results cannot be taken to be truly normal, the determination of parameters by means of relationships which are based on the assumed validity of the Gaussian law, and therefore also the use of parametric tests, will be rather doubtful, and the utility of the conclusions will depend on the sensitivity of the respective tests to non-normality of the distribution of the analytical results. In such a case it becomes necessary to apply tests which are not based on the assumption of some probability distribution, and do not make use of any estimates of parameters. Most of these non-parametric methods [29], of which quite a large number are already known, are applied in those cases where enough experimental material is available. It is also obvious that these methods, which are not based on any assumptions of a distribution of the results, are generally of lower sensitivity, i.e. they will show a difference to be significant only if it is greater than in the case of parametric methods. For this reason also, non-parametric methods find less application in analytical practice. Here we shall describe only two of them: one for the comparison of two series of parallel determinations carried out by different methods, and a second which is very well suited for determining a systematic error.

Table 4.20. Critical Values of Difference of Serial Numbers for the Non-parametric Test of two Series of Determinations [34a]

n \ α	0.01	0.02	0.05
5	18	16	15
6	27	24	23
7	37	34	32
8	49	46	43
9	63	59	56
10	79	74	71
11	97	91	87
12	116	110	105
13	137	130	125
14	160	152	147
15	185	176	170
16	212	202	196
17	241	230	223
18	271	259	252
19	303	291	282
20	338	324	315

The first method, used to compare two analytical procedures, involves arrangement of the results according to magnitude irrespective of the method to which they belong. The analytical results thus arranged are then numbered in rising order (1, 2 ..n: if there are several analytical results of the same magnitude, the arithmetic mean of the corresponding numbers is ascribed to them all). The serial numbers for each method are then added, and their difference is calculated and compared with values given in Table 4.20 for a chosen value of α and the given number of determinations. If both methods give results of equal accuracy within the limits of random error, the difference of serial numbers will be small, while if the two methods give differing results, the sum of the serial numbers of the two methods will be large, the difference will exceed the tabulated value, and the assumption that both methods give equal results cannot be upheld [29].

As an example of the application of this non-parametric test, let us compare the two series of results of the iodometric determination of ferric ions in iron(III) ammonium citrate, mentioned earlier.

The difference of sums of the serial numbers is $100 - 36 = 64$: for $n = 8$ and $\alpha = 0.01$ Table 4.20 shows a value of 49. The actual difference is larger than the critical value: in full agreement with the parametric t-test, the non-parametric test proves a significant difference in the results of the two series of determinations.

A Fe, %	Serial number	B Fe, %	Serial number
13.29	1	13.86	10
13.36	4	13.99	16
13.32	3	13.88	11
13.53	7	13.91	14
13.56	8	13.89	12.5
13.43	5.5	13.94	15
13.30	2	13.80	9
13.43	5.5	13.89	12.5
$\bar{x}_A = 13.402$	36	$\bar{x}_B = 13.895$	100

The second method of non-parametric comparison of two methods, specially suitable for the elucidation of systematic errors, consists of comparing each time two analytical results obtained for the same sample. If the results obtained with the one method are systematically larger or smaller than the results obtained with the second method, i.e. the differences of pairs of determinations are prevalently positive or negative, then the two methods cannot be equal. Taking for example two methods denoted A and B, let us for each pair of determinations subtract result A from result B and investigate only the number of positive or negative differences. The test then consists of comparing the number of positive and of negative differences with the values given in Table 4.21. If there is no difference between the two methods, then the probability of occurrence of the positive or negative sign should always be 0.5 according to the binomial theorem: the number of positive differences should therefore differ from the number of negative differences only within the limits of random error. In the reverse case the difference between the two methods must be considered. Let k_1 denote the number of positive or negative differences, depending on which number is larger, and k_2 the smaller number. The two methods give equal results, with a probability of $\alpha = 0.05$ or 0.01, if the number of differences of equal sign is equal to or smaller than the value of k_1 given in Table 4.21 (or if it is equal to or larger than k_2 in Table 4.21). This test may also be

Table 4.21. Critical Values of k_1 and k_2 for the Number of Positive or Negative Differences in the Non-parametric Test of two Different Methods

n	$\alpha = 0.05$		$\alpha = 0.01$	
	k_1	k_2	k_1	k_2
5	5	0	5	0
6	5	1	6	0
7	6	1	7	0
8	7	1	7	1
9	7	2	8	1
10	8	2	9	1
11	9	2	10	1
12	9	3	10	2
13	10	3	11	2
14	11	3	12	2
15	11	4	12	3
16	12	4	13	3
17	12	5	14	3
18	13	5	14	4
19	14	5	15	4
20	14	6	16	4
22	16	6	17	5
24	17	7	18	6
26	18	8	19	7
28	19	9	21	7
30	20	10	22	8
32	21	11	23	9

applied to the search for a systematic error which is so small that it cannot be detected by the t-test; the present method will show it precisely because of its systematic occurrence, if the positive and negative differences of the experimental and true values are counted.

Let us demonstrate this method by means of the following example. The efficiency of insulin (mean value 23.5 units/mg) is determined by biological and polarographic means: the two methods are based on totally different principles and their reproducibility differs to such a degree that the t-test cannot be used to compare the results obtained with these two methods. The methods were compared by determining the effects of 32 insulin doses, the results being compared mutually in pairs [58].

Although in 18 of the 32 possible cases the polarographic method gives a higher result, yet the differences may be explained by random errors for $\alpha = 0.01$ and $\alpha = 0.05$. From a practical point of view it is more important that the absolute differences between results obtained by means of the two methods should not be large: the mean relative difference is $\dfrac{0.975 \times 100}{23.559}\ \% = 4.1\ \%$, while the relative error of the biological determination of insulin efficiency was estimated as $\pm 10\%$.

4.23 Sequential analysis

The elucidation of systematic errors by the use of the numbers of positive and negative deviations has the disadvantage that the reliability of this non-parametric test depends to some extent on the number of results, i.e. the appraisal of a small number of results may lead to erroneous conclusions. Because of this well known fact it is usual to carry out many more determinations than are essential. This drawback may be avoided by means of *sequential analysis* [34], which makes it possible to distinguish between three possibilities.

(1) The number of positive and negative deviations corresponds to the existence of purely random errors.

(2) The number of deviations in one direction is substantially greater than the number of de-

Efficiency of insulin, units/mg		
biological	polarographic	difference
25.2	25.7	+0.5
24.1	24.8	+0.7
23.7	22.0	−1.7
23.7	24.0	+1.3
23.7	23.9	+0.2
23.3	24.5	+1.2
24.5	21.9	−2.6
23.5	22.3	−1.2
23.7	21.7	−2.0
23.6	22.1	−1.5
23.2	23.5	+0.3
22.6	24.2	+1.6
22.6	23.2	+0.6
23.8	25.4	+1.6
22.9	23.4	+0.5
22.8	23.1	+0.3
22.0	21.8	−0.2
22.5	23.8	+1.3
22.6	22.5	+0.9
23.6	24.3	+0.7
23.6	22.2	−1.4
23.4	23.8	+0.4
22.5	24.3	+1.8
23.3	22.0	−1.3
24.6	23.0	−1.4
23.3	22.7	−0.6
24.6	23.2	−1.4
24.3	23.8	−0.5
24.0	24.6	+0.6
24.5	24.5	0.0
24.3	23.0	−1.3
23.9	24.5	+0.6
		mean 0.975

Mean value of the
biological determination: 23.559 units/mg

13 differences are negative in sign
18 differences are positive in sign
 1 difference is zero.

viations in the other, a fact which may be explained by the presence of systematic errors.

(3) The number of determinations performed is insufficient for a reliable appraisal of the analytical method.

Sequential analysis is carried out by graphical means: therefore the test is very illustrative and allows the individual results to be included each time a new result is obtained. This is of great advantage in practical analysis, because individual samples may thus be analysed in the order they are obtained in the laboratory. Moreover, it can be seen immediately after each new double determination whether the number of results already suffices or whether more are needed.

The procedure is the same as with the preceding test, i.e. several samples of the same material are analysed by means of two methods, and the difference of the two results in each pair is calculated, taking note of the sign. The frequency, i.e. the ratio between the number of deviations of a given sign and the total number of determinations, is denoted by p; it must be expected that the number of positive and negative deviations will be equal as long as there is no systematic error involved, i.e. $p = 0.5$. The results of the pairs of analyses with which the test is being carried out are obviously only a random selection, and for this reason the conclusions drawn from them hold only with a certain probability. Therefore the degree of significance of the final result must first be decided upon, i.e. the maximum probability which shall be permitted for an erroneous conclusion. Such an erroneous conclusion may originate on the one hand by discard of the method which is in fact the accurate one (the probability of such an erroneous conclusion is denoted α) while, on the other hand, a method may be thought to be accurate, which in fact is the inaccurate one (the probability of this conclusion is β). As a rule it is presumed that $\alpha = \beta = 0.05$ and only in the case that a wrong conclusion might lead to grave consequences do we select 0.01 as the degree of significance for α or β. Two values p_A and p_B must also be selected. These values should be arranged symmetrically with respect to $p = 0.50$, and it is demanded that the frequency of deviations of positive sign be located between these two values. Selecting for example $p_A = 0.25$ and $p_B = 0.75$, one is in fact testing whether the frequency of the

Table 4.22. Values of h_1, h_2, s_1, s_2 for Plotting the Sequential Analysis Diagram

p_A	p_B	$\alpha =$ $\beta =$		0.01 0.01	0.01 0.05		0.05 0.01		0.05 0.05
		s_1	s_2	$h_1 = h_2$	h_1	h_2	h_1	h_2	$h_1 = h_2$
0.05	0.95	2.2	7.8	1.6	1.0	1.6	1.6	1.0	1.0
0.10	0.90	2.7	7.3	2.1	1.4	2.1	2.1	1.4	1.3
0.15	0.85	3.0	7.0	2.6	1.7	2.6	2.6	1.7	1.7
0.20	0.80	3.4	6.6	3.3	2.2	3.3	3.3	2.2	2.1
0.25	0.75	3.7	6.3	4.2	2.7	4.2	4.2	2.7	2.7
0.30	0.70	4.0	6.0	5.4	3.5	5.4	5.4	3.5	3.5
0.35	0.65	4.2	5.8	7.4	4.8	7.4	7.4	4.8	4.8
0.40	0.60	4.5	5.5	11.4	7.4	11.2	11.2	7.4	7.3
0.45	0.55	4.7	5.3	23.0	14.9	22.8	22.8	14.9	14.7

positive deviations has a minimum of 0.25 and a maximum of 0.75. If the actual frequency of the positive deviations lies outside these limits, the method must be assumed to be inferior to the comparison method. Obviously the values of p_A and p_B influence the "severity" of this decision: if values of p_A and p_B were selected close to $p = 0.50$, a larger number of pairs of analytical results would be needed, as a rule, to arrive at a final conclusion. On the other hand it thus becomes possible to prove whether the actual frequency value is really close to the theoretical frequency of $p = 0.50$. Table 4.22 shows, for the selected values of α and β, p_A and p_B, the corresponding values of h_1 and h_2, i.e. sections on the y-axis for $x = 0$, and the values of s_1 and s_2, i.e. sections added to h_1 and h_2 for $x = 10$, the total number of deviations being plotted on the x-axis and the number of positive deviations on the y-axis.

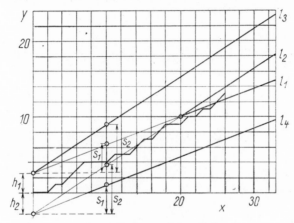

FIG. 4.10. Sequential analysis.

Tho total number, of course, includes only those deviations for which it can be proved that their mutual differences are not unduly large. The plotting and application of the diagram is to be seen in Fig. 4.10.

The number of pairs of determinations is plotted on the x-axis, the number of deviations of positive sign is plotted on the y-axis: a broken line thus originates when each result with a negative deviation is plotted horizontally one unit to the right, and each positive deviation is plotted as a diagonal line through one unit square up and to the right. This plotting is continued until the broken line intersects one of the straight lines which form the limits of the diagram.

If the broken line intersects the straight line l_4, it may be stated that that analytical method gives results which are too low, with the probability α (i.e. the frequency of the lower results is p_B, but never $p = 0.50$): if the broken line intersects the straight line l_3, it may similarly be concluded that the results of that method are too high. In both cases the method tested must be discarded as being inferior to the comparison method. If the broken line intersects the straight lines l_1 or l_2, i.e. it passes through the central conical part of the diagram, then the method in question may be assumed to be equal in accuracy to the standard method. If the broken line intersects none of the limiting straight lines in the diagram, then the number of results is too low for a reliable conclusion, and more analyses are required.

The example in Fig. 4.10 shows the comparison of two methods for the micro-determination of iodine in biological material, the following signs of deviations having been found:

$$- - + - + + + - - - + - - + + - + + - - - + - + - + +$$

The test was carried out for the values $\alpha = \beta = 0.05$, $p_A = 0.25$, $p_B = 0.75$. After 26 pairs of analyses the broken line intersects the straight line l_1 and passes through the central conical part of the diagram. For this reason the method tested is assumed to be equal in accuracy to the standard method. Figure 4.10 shows that, under the conditions mentioned, a positive conclusion about the method tested cannot be expected with less than 22 results, while a negative conclusion could be achieved with only 8 results, if all deviations had the same sign.

Chapter 5

GRAPHICAL AND NUMERICAL METHODS

5.1 Calibration graphs

Most physico-chemical methods used in analytical chemistry utilize the dependence of a certain measurable quantity (e.g. the height of a polarographic wave, absorbance, pH, potential, conductivity, refractive index, optical rotation) on the concentration of the substances to be determined in solution. This dependence may be written

$$y = f(c_X) \qquad (5.1)$$

where y is the value of the quantity measured and c_x is the corresponding concentration of the component to be determined. More rarely do we carry out the determination by measuring y and then calculating directly the concentration of the required component, using a tabulated "specific" or "molar" quantity determined beforehand once and for all by experimental means (e.g. the polarimetric glucose determination). Mostly the functional dependence between the measured quantity and concentration of the solution is determined experimentally, and the relationship obtained is frequently treated graphically. Such a curve of the relationship between the concentration of the substance determined and the quantity measured is called a *calibration graph*. In other cases, especially with methods the results of which depend on ill-defined conditions of measurement, a calibration curve cannot be prepared definitively but has to be constructed anew for each analysis. Two great advantages of the graphic method are its illustrative character and that it has some degree of compensation of the influence of systematic as well as of random errors. On the other hand, however, the final result is subject not only to the errors of the measurement proper, but also to the error of the experimental determination of the relationship between y and c_x (which may frequently be influenced by the purity of the standard employed) and to errors of reading from the graph.

The procedure in constructing a calibration graph involves the preparation of solutions of different concentrations of the component to be determined, the concentration being selected so as to ensure that the concentration of the most dilute solution is lower, and that of the most concentrated one is higher, than the concentration range in which the concentration of the solution to be analysed is expected to be. The concentrations of the other solutions should be distributed regularly between these two extremes.

An important question is that of the number of points, i.e. solutions prepared and measured, from which the calibration curve is constructed. Obviously, the rule "the more, the better" holds here also: however, the preparation of a large number of solutions and performance of many measurements is difficult and laborious. Even in routine work, however, and even if the relationship concerned is strictly linear, a calibration graph should be constructed from at least five points: curves, especially if they are substantially different from a straight line, should be constructed from a proportionately larger number of points, especially in the vicinity of extreme and inflexion points. Obviously the entire analytical procedure and measurement is carried out with all the standard solutions under conditions identical as far as possible to those of the sample analysis. The measured values of y are then plotted in the graph against the respective concentration values, the rectangular cartesian co-ordinate system being most frequently used.

Although it is said that the values plotted in the calibration graph have been measured for certain values of c_x, it must be noted that these values are also known only approximately, weighing, dilution, etc. being operations which, as already shown, are subject to certain errors. If, therefore, the individual points do not lie in a single straight line, it is assumed that this is caused by errors in the preparation and measurement of the solutions. For this reason a curve is drawn through the points instead of the individual points being joined by straight lines (which would give a broken line): in this way, errors in the determination of the relationship between y and c_x are compensated.

Another important problem is *legibility of the graph:* the most legible ones are formed by a straight line passing through the origin of the co-ordinate system and forming an angle of 45° with the axes. Straight lines running practically parallel to the axes are not suitable for reading: their slope may, however, be adjusted by suitable selecting the scales. Complicated curves with a high degree of curvature also make exact reading difficult.

Let us now discuss the precision of reading from a graph. The absolute error of reading from a graph constructed on millimetre-paper is about ±0.25 mm: even the most carefully made graph will not permit reading with a precision better than 0.1 mm. The relative error occurring on reading from a graph, especially if small values are being read, may easily achieve rather a large magnitude, and of course this error must be added to the other errors of the determination. However, when all the errors which may possibly occur are being added, the result of the addition is, in fact, the "maximum" error: this occurs in practice only in extreme cases, as already mentioned in section 1.6. Details about calibration curves will be found in the monograph [10].

In concluding this section, let us mention the case of *measurements of low reproducibility*. The reproducibility of these measurements may be so low that they cannot be expected to correspond to Eq. 5.1, but rather to the relationship

$$\bar{y} = f(c_x) \qquad (5.2)$$

according to which an entire distribution of y values, with a mean value of $\bar{y}$, corresponds to each value of c_x. In such a case a smooth curve cannot be drawn through the experimental points, and they should rather be delimited with a so-called *contour ellipse*. This case sometimes occurs in trace analysis. For spectrographic analysis, HOLDT [67] has solved this problem by means of the scatter-diagram method. In such a case Eq. 5.2 must be obtained by means of the linear regression method, which will be described in section 5.4.

5.2 Numerical and graphical interpolation

When a functional relationship is being determined by experimental means, e.g. the dependence of some quantity y on the concentration of the component determined c_x (Eq. 5.1), only a limited number of values of y is measured. Let us denote these by $y_0, y_1, y_2 \ldots y_n$, these being values of the quantity y corresponding to the concentrations c_0, c_1, c_2 to c_n. In practical work it is frequently necessary to find the concentration c_x corresponding to a measured value of y which lies between two values measured in the experimental determination of the functional relationship. The procedure by which this problem is solved is called *interpolation*.

When the functional relationship is presented in graphical form, and if we are satisfied with an approximate result, it is relatively easy to obtain the value of y corresponding to any value of c_x within the range measured. Such a reading from a graph is called graphical interpolation.

For more precise interpolation, numerical methods are preferable. If the function is linear, or if it can be assumed to be approximately linear between two close values of y, the very simple procedure of linear interpolation in used. This procedure is well-known from the calculation of logarithms by use of tables with relative parts ("partes proportionales"). Practically the same method is employed if no relative parts, tabulated for certain differences, are available, i.e. the relative parts must be calculated.

For example, the concentration of a zinc salt solution with a polarographic wave-height of $i_d = 58$ mm is calculated from a table listing the relationship between the height of the polarographic wave and the zinc ion concentration:

Because $58 - 44 = 14$, we obtain $c_x = 2 \times 10^{-32} + 1 \times 10^{-3} \times \dfrac{14}{22} = 2.64 \times 10^{-3}$. It is similarly possible to subtract from the larger value, i.e. $66 - 58 = 8$ and $c_x = 3 \times 10^{-3} - 1 \times 10^{-3} \times \dfrac{8}{22} = 2.64 \times 10^{-3}$.

c_x	i_d	$\varDelta$
1×10^{-3}	22	22
2×10^{-3}	44	22
3×10^{-3}	66	22
4×10^{-3}	87	21
5×10^{-3}	109	22

Graphical interpolation is mainly useful in those cases where a graph is constructed: numerical interpolation, which is more accurate, is of advantage if the experimental values are tabulated and if a linear relationship may correctly be assumed to hold in the range in which the interpolation is required. Although non-linear interpolation is also possible, e.g. by means of Newton's formula, it is somewhat more complicated and in analytical practice is always replaced by graphical interpolation.

The precision of results obtained by means of interpolation is, of course, limited by the experimental errors of determining the functional relationship.

the error of the measurement proper, and in graphical interpolation by the error of reading the graph. With numerical interpolation there are practically only experimental errors, and the error of interpolation is negligible.

With physico-chemical measurements, use is sometimes also made of *extrapolation*, i.e. interpolation outside the range of values for which the measurements were done. Obviously this method is suitable only if the curve of the relationship $y = f(c_x)$ is smooth, and if there is no reason to assume any sudden changes within the interval measured, and if extrapolation is made to a value which is not too far away from the interval measured. Nevertheless every extrapolation, numerical or graphical, is rather a risky matter.

5.3 Numerical and graphical determination of the point of inflexion

Searching for the *point of inflexion* of a curve is a task which occurs frequently in practical analytical chemistry, as for example the point of equivalence of potentiometric titration is characterized by the inflexion of the titration curve, i.e. in which the indicating electrode potential E, is plotted against volume of solution added, V. Using either graphical or numerical methods, the starting point is the fact that the first derivative dE/dV of the function $E = f(V)$ has a maximum value at the inflexion point in a certain local region, while the second derivative is zero.

In the graphical solution the derivative is replaced by the ratio of differences: the value of $\Delta E/\Delta V$ is plotted in relation to V, and the amount of solution V is found for which the value of $\Delta E/\Delta V$ is largest. An example of the graphical determination of the point of inflexion is given in Fig. 3.1. Another possibility of determining the point of equivalence of a potentiometric titration, by use of a plotted titration curve, consists of searching for the intersection of the curve with a straight line which delimits equal areas above and below the curve. This method is very easy to carry out with a transparent ruler, and is specially suitable for symmetrical and regular titration curves (Fig. 5.1).

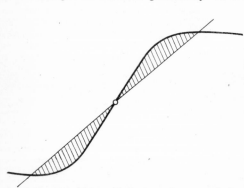

FIG. 5.1. Point of inflexion of symmetrical titration curve.

Numerical determination of the titrant consumption at the point of equivalence is quicker, simpler and more precise than the graphical procedure. Frequently a very simple procedure is adopted when small and regular portions ΔV of the volumetric solution have been added, the consumption being calculated according to the relationship

$$V = V_m + \frac{1}{2} \Delta V_m \qquad (5.3)$$

where V_m is the consumption of volumetric solution after which the increment of solution ΔV_m caused the greatest change ΔE; alternatively the relationship

$$V = V_n \tag{5.4}$$

may be used, where V_n is that consumption of the solution for which the preceding and following increments ΔV caused roughly equal changes ΔE, these changes being larger than for any other increments of the same size. A precise and relatively simple procedure involves the following scheme:

It then holds, that

$$V = V_m + \Delta V \frac{\Delta^2 E_{n-1}}{\Delta^2 E_{n-1} + \Delta^2 E_n} \tag{5.5}$$

In a more illustrative manner the use of these three relationships may be shown by the example of the determination of sodium chloride in solution by means of argentometric titration: the indicating electrode is silver, the reference electrode is the saturated calomel electrode: three equal aliquots are titrated with 0.1 M silver nitrate.

V	E	ΔE	$\Delta^2 E$
V_0	E_0		
V_1	E_1	ΔE_0	$\Delta^2 E_0$
V_2	E_2	ΔE_1	
.	.	.	.
.	.	.	.
.	.	.	.
V_{n-1}	E_{n-1}		
V_n	E_n	ΔE_{n-1}	$\Delta^2 E_{n-1}$
V_{n+1}	E_{n+1}	ΔE_n	$\Delta^2 E_n$
V_{n+2}	E_{n+2}	ΔE_{n+1}	

	V_m (ml)	E	ΔE	$\Delta^2 E$
Titration 1	15.1	198		
	15.2	201		
	15.3	245	44	$+7$
	15.4	296	51	-47
	15.5	300	4	
	15.6	303		$54 = \lvert \Delta^2 E \rvert$
Titration 2	15.1	196		
	15.2	200		
	15.3	209	9	$+50$
	15.4	268	59	-11
	15.5	316	48	
	15.6	319		$61 = \lvert \Delta^2 E \rvert$
Titration 3	15.1	197		
	15.2	202		
	15.3	228	26	$+15$
	15.4	269	41	-13
	15.5	297	28	
	15.6	306		$28 = \lvert \Delta^2 E \rvert$

Using the simpler Eqs. 5.3 and 5.4 we find the consumption as follows:

Titration 1	15.30 ml
Titration 2	15.40 ml
Titration 3	15.35 ml
Mean	15.35 ml

By use of the scheme above and Eq. 5.5, the consumption is found to be

$$\text{Titration 1.} \quad 15.30 + 0.1 \times \frac{7}{54} = 15.31 \text{ ml}$$

$$\text{Titration 2.} \quad 15.30 + 0.1 \times \frac{50}{61} = 15.38 \text{ ml}$$

$$\text{Titration 3.} \quad 15.30 + 0.1 \times \frac{15}{28} = 15.35 \text{ ml}$$

Mean	15.34 ml

It is evident that the results are almost the same.

5.4 Linear regression

The preceding sections have shown the great advantages of a carefully constructed graph, especially if interpolations are to be carried out frequently. It has also been shown that the error of graphical interpolation may be rather large, and that together with the experimental errors it may distort the accuracy of the final result. It is therefore sometimes better to use the functional relationship and to replace the set of measured values by a curve which is the "best" curve drawn through these points.

Let us first consider a linear relationship of the form

$$y = a + bx \tag{5.6}$$

where y is the dependent and x the independent variable, and a, b are coefficients. In the sense of the present discussion the "independent" variable will always be the one determined by experimental means, but of such a character that it must be assumed to be either free from error or subject to an error substantially smaller than that of the dependent variable. If the coefficients a and b are known it is easy to calculate the value of y for any value of x. If the corresponding values of y were known precisely for several values of x, it would become possible to calculate the values of a and b, simply by calculating a system of equations with two unknown quantities. An empirical formula would thus be obtained, the only problem being how to utilize information from all the equations to calculate the two unknown quantities a and b. Since however the values of y are generally distorted by the influence of experimental errors, such a calculation would be very imprecise. The coefficients can be determined reliably with respect to the errors of the variable y by using the principle of maximum confidence for variables having a normal distribution. This leads to the determination of the *regression curve* for the regression of y on x. On this principle the influence of random errors is compensated by minimizing the sum of squares of deviations of the individual points from the regression curve (deviations are measured parallel to the y axis). It should be noted that the position of the individual variables is very important, because for the regression of x on y a different line would be obtained. Regression is of course a wide concept, including also cases where an entire probability distribution of y corresponds to one value of x.

The coefficients of Eq. 5.6 are determined best by arranging the results of measurements according to the following scheme, assuming each time only the experimental value of y for each x value:

Experiment No.	x_i	y_i	x_i^2	$x_i \cdot y_i$	Y_i	$y_i - Y_i$	$(y_i - Y_i)^2$
1	x_1	y_1	x_1^2	$x_1 \cdot y_1$	Y_1	$y_1 - Y_1$	$(y_1 - Y_1)^2$
2	x_2	y_2	x_2^2	$x_2 \cdot y_2$	Y_2	$y_2 - Y_2$	$(y_2 - Y_2)^2$
3	x_3	y_3	x_3^2	$x_3 \cdot y_3$	Y_3	$y_3 - Y_3$	$(y_3 - Y_3)^2$
.	.	.	.	.	.	.	.
.	.	.	.	.	.	.	.
.	.	.	.	.	.	.	.
n	x_n	y_n	x_n^2	$x_n \cdot y_n$	Y_n	$y_n - Y_n$	$(y_n - Y_n)^2$
	$\Sigma(x_i)$ $[\Sigma(x_i)]^2$	$\Sigma(y_i)$	$\Sigma(x_i^2)$	$\Sigma x_i \cdot y_i$			$\Sigma(y_i - Y_i)^2$

Note: y_i = values obtained experimentally, Y_i = regression values

The slope of the regression line b, also called the *regression coefficient*, is calculated from the so-called normal equations by means of the relationship

$$b = \frac{\Sigma(x) \cdot \Sigma(y) - n \Sigma(x \cdot y)}{[\Sigma(x)]^2 - n \Sigma(x^2)} \tag{5.7}$$

The second coefficient a, called the *shift* (or *intercept*) *of the regression line*, is usually obtained by substituting $\bar{y} = \frac{1}{n} \Sigma(y)$ and $\bar{x} = \frac{1}{n} \Sigma(x)$ in Eq. 5.6, i.e.

$$a = \frac{1}{n} [\Sigma(y) - b \cdot \Sigma(x)] \tag{5.8}$$

The estimate of the standard deviation of scatter around the regression line is given by the relationship

$$s_{x,y} = \sqrt{\frac{\Sigma(y_i - Y_i)^2}{n - 2}} \tag{5.9}$$

where y_i is, for a given value x_i, the experimental value of the dependent variable, while Y_i is the same value but calculated from the regression equation. The estimate of the standard deviations of the regression coefficient s_b, and of the shift, s_a, are given by the relationships

$$s_b = \frac{s_{x,y}}{\sqrt{\Sigma x^2 - \bar{x} \Sigma x}} \tag{5.10}$$

$$s_a = \sqrt{\frac{\Sigma x^2}{n \Sigma x^2 - (\Sigma x)^2}} \tag{5.11}$$

Another important characteristic, usually employed when studying the dependence of two variables, is the *correlation coefficient* r:

$$r = \frac{\Sigma(x - \bar{x})(y - \bar{y})}{\sqrt{\Sigma(x - \bar{x})^2 (y - \bar{y})^2}} = \frac{n \Sigma xy - \Sigma x \Sigma y}{\sqrt{[n \Sigma x^2 - (\Sigma x)^2][n \Sigma y^2 - (\Sigma y)^2]}} \tag{5.12}$$

The correlation coefficient characterizes the degree of mutual dependence between two variables: it may achieve values from -1 to $+1$, the sign $+$

holding for direct and − for indirect relationships; its value is zero if the two variables are independent of each other and its value is +1 or −1 if there is a functional, i.e. a very close relationship between the two. Obviously the calculation according to Eq. 5.12 is only an estimate, and it may differ from the true value of the correlation coefficient. Therefore critical values are listed in Table 5.1, i.e. values which the correlation coefficient may achieve for a given number of results and a probability of 0.95 or 0.99, even if the two variables are absolutely mutually independent [8].

Table 5.1. Critical Values of the Correlation Coefficient

n	$\alpha = 0.95$	$\alpha = 0.99$	n	$\alpha = 0.95$	$\alpha = 0.99$
5	0.75	0.87	18	0.44	0.56
6	0.71	0.83	20	0.42	0.54
7	0.67	0.80	25	0.38	0.49
8	0.63	0.77	30	0.35	0.45
9	0.60	0.74	40	0.30	0.39
10	0,58	0.71	50	0.27	0.35
12	0.53	0.66	60	0.25	0.33
14	0.50	0.62	80	0.22	0.28
16	0.47	0.59	100	0.20	0.25

In analytical practice, calculation of the regression curve is important mainly because it not only allows a systematic error to be recognized, but also makes it possible to find out whether this is a *constant* or a *proportional systematic error* (i.e. dependent on the concentration of the component determined). From Eq. 5.6, where y is the amount found by experiment and x the true amount of the component to be determined, the values of the coefficients should ideally by $a = 0$ and $b = 1$, i.e. it should hold that $y = x$[101, 102]. If the value of the coefficient differs in a statistically significant degree from zero, then there is a constant systematic error, while a statistically significant difference of the value of b from unity indicates a proportional systematic error. These observations are very useful, especially if the error must be removed by a modification of the experimental conditions. In such a case it is certainly useful to know in which part of the analytical procedure the systematic error may originate.

A constant error may be caused by inaccuracies of volumetric glassware or of weights. A positive constant error may also be caused by presence of the component determined, as an impurity in those reagents of which equal amounts are added in each analysis. Such errors are easy to avoid, e.g. by calibrating the glassware and weights or by subtracting a blank experiment value. A proportional systematic error might be caused by an incorrectly determined titre of a volumetric solution (which, however, would be a gross error): more probably such an error will be due to imperfect stoicheiometry of the analytical reaction employed, or by physical influences, e.g. adsorption on a precipitate, solubility of precipitates, or variation in establishment of an equilibrium.

Thus it is very important to determine the statistical significance of deviations of the coefficients a and b from zero and unity respectively. A very elegant procedure, easily carried out graphically, has been described by MANDEL and LINNING [77]. These authors have found that the values a and b are always in slight negative correlation. By constructing the contour ellipse for the correlation of these two coefficients we may find easily whether the values of $a = 0$ and $b = 1$ are located within it. To construct the contour ellipse, a rectangle is constructed in the co-ordinate system a, b, its sides being $l_a = \sqrt{2F \cdot s_a^2}$ and $l_b = \sqrt{2F \cdot s_b^2}$, F being found in tables of the Snedecor distribution for $v_1 = 2$ and $v_2 = n - 2$ and for the selected α value (e.g. 0.95 or 0.99). Now a distance of $d_b = \sqrt{4zs_{xy}^2F/\Sigma x\Sigma x^2 + z}$ is plotted in the perpendicular direction to both sides, and the distance $d_a = d_b \cdot l_a/l_b$ is plotted in the horizontal direction, z being equal to $\sqrt{n\Sigma x^2}$. The ellipse is then easily plotted as shown in Fig. 5.2.

If the horizontal line for $b = 1$ intersects the ellipse there is no proportional error, while if the horizontal line for $a = 0$ intersects the ellipse there is no constant error.

Determining the presence of a systematic error by studying the relation between the amounts "taken" and "found" of the component determined is not the only application of linear regression in analytical chemistry. It has already been mentioned in section 5.1 that inferior reproducibility of the measurement may sometimes cause a surface of scattered points to be obtained instead of a smooth and straight calibration line. In such a case it is essential to calculate the relationship by determining the coefficients of the regression line and the correlation coefficient. HOLDT has shown for the case of spectral analysis [67] that construction of a scatter diagram and delimiting the area of experimental points with a contour ellipse from calculated values is similar to the procedure described above.

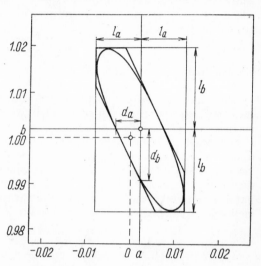

FIG. 5.2. Mandel and Linning's method.

The calculation of equation parameters for a non-linear relationship is somewhat more difficult. For example, when determining the coefficients of the equation

$$y = a + bx + cx^2 + dx^3$$

from measured values of y for different values of x, the following procedure is involved. Arrange the experimental values in a table:

x	y	x^2	x^3 ... x^6	xy	x^2y	x^3y
x_1	y_1	x_1^2	x_1^3 ... x_1^6	xy_1	$x_1^2y_1$	$x_1^3x_1$
.	.	.	.	.	.	.
.	.	.	.	.	.	.
.	.	.	.	.	.	.
x_n	y_n	x_n^2	x_n^3　x_n^6	x_ny_n	$x_n^2y_n$	$x_n^3y_n$
Σx	Σy	Σx^2	Σx^3 ... Σx^6	Σxy	Σx^2y	Σx^3y

and for the condition of the least sum of squares set up normalized equations

$$an + b\Sigma x + c\Sigma x^2 + d\Sigma x^3 - \Sigma y = 0$$
$$a\Sigma x + b\Sigma x^2 + c\Sigma x^3 + d\Sigma x^4 - \Sigma x_y = 0$$
$$a\Sigma x^2 + b\Sigma x^3 + c\Sigma x^4 + d\Sigma x^5 - \Sigma x^2 y = 0$$
$$a\Sigma x^3 + b\Sigma x^4 + c\Sigma x^5 + d\Sigma x^6 - \Sigma x^3 y = 0$$

This gives four equations of four unknown quantities, which have then to be solved. In practical analytical chemistry, non-linear relationships are usually treated graphically [10].

5.5 The final result of chemical analysis

The final result of chemical analysis should always be the mean of at least two analyses carried out independently of each other. Calculation of the mean of several parallel analyses is a very simple matter.

If, however, a certain element is determined by means of several methods, each of which offers results which are accurate (or at least the t-test proves no significant differences), but the reproducibility of the results differs, then it is better not to calculate the final result as a simple arithmetic mean, but instead to take into account the reliability of results obtained by different methods by calculating the *weighted mean* $\bar{\bar{x}}$:

$$\bar{\bar{x}} = \frac{p_1\bar{x}_1 + p_2\bar{x}_2 + \ldots + p_k\bar{x}_k}{p_1 + p_2 + \ldots + p_k} = \frac{\Sigma p_i\bar{x}_i}{\Sigma p} \tag{5.13}$$

where the values of $p_1, p_2 \ldots p_1$ are the weightings of the results, in this case of the means $x_1, x_2 \ldots x_k$ calculated from the experimental results obtained by means of the first, second, … kth analytical method. The values of the individual weightings may be determined in different ways: if the scatter values σ_i^2 ($i = 1, 2, \ldots k$) of the results of determinations carried out by the different methods are either known or can be estimated, the following formula is used

$$p_i = \frac{n_i}{\sigma_i^2} = \frac{1}{\sigma_{x_i}^2} \tag{5.14}$$

where n_i is the number of determinations carried out by the ith method and σ_i^2 is the scatter of the mean x_i. If, however, the scatter values are unknown and cannot be estimated, but may be assumed to be equal for all methods, the relationship

$$p_i = n_i \tag{5.15}$$

is used and Eq. 5.13 becomes

$$\bar{\bar{x}} = \frac{\Sigma n_i\bar{x}_i}{\Sigma n_i} \tag{5.16}$$

The estimate of *scatter of a "weighted" mean* is given by

$$s_{\bar{x}}^2 = \frac{\Sigma s_i^2(n_i - 1)}{(\Sigma n_i) - k} \tag{5.17}$$

The use of a "weighted" mean is justified because results, obtained by means of a method of better reproducibility or as the mean of a large number of analyses, are more reliable, and should therefore have a greater influence on the value of the result. It should be added that this method of homogenizing results obtained by means of methods of different precision, has been derived by means of the least squares method in a manner similar to the derivation of the arithmetic mean or of the coefficients of regression lines.

5.6 Expression of the results of chemical analyses

It is surprising that analysts, who frequently expend much time and effort on the performance of an analysis, are frequently less careful when setting down the results of the analysis. In conventional work, it has not yet become the habit to express results together with data concerning their precision, either in the form of a confidence interval, e.g. $(8.38 - 8.46)\%$ or by using the absolute error, e.g. $8.42 \pm 0.04\%$, or with an expression of the relative error, e.g. $8.42\% \pm 0.47\%$ rel. Therefore, if it is the custom to express an analytical result by means of a single numerical value, it should at least become a strict rule that the result should be given with only one decimal more than can be guaranteed.

For example a result calculated as the means of two determinations of silicon dioxide, 46.12% SiO_2 and 46.29% SiO_2 should be stated as 46.2% SiO_2, because in the precise mean (46.205%) only units of per cent can be guaranteed: in another example, the determination of traces of vanadium where the results are 0.0031% V and 0.0074% V, the result should be given as 0.005% V (the arithmetic mean is $x_a = 0.00525$, the geometric mean is $x_g = 0.00479\%$), because from the experimental results even this value cannot, in actual fact, be guaranteed. The mean result of two aluminium determinations, 21.96% Al and 22.05% Al, should be stated as 22.00%, because units of tenths of per cent can be guaranteed; although the two analyses differ in actual units of per cent, their true difference is only 0.09%. The hundredths obviously cannot be guaranteed, and they are therefore the last decimal quotable.

If results are given with a smaller number of decimals, there is the problem of *rounding off*. Results are rounded off by leaving out all decimals which are not to appear in the final result. The last decimal remains unchanged if followed by a digit lower than 5 (rounding off downwards) and is increased by one if followed by a digit greater than 5 (rounding off upwards). A five, if followed by any digit other than zero, is rounded off upwards. However, if the last digit which is to be used in the result is followed by a five and this is followed by zeros only (e.g. if this five is the last digit of a quotient when the division had no residue), we round off by increasing the last digit to be used in the result by one if it is even, and leaving it unchanged if it is odd, so that rounding off a five always results in an even number (divisible by two).

For example numbers from 6.8150 to 6.8250 are rounded off to 6.82, but 6.8251 should be rounded off to 6.83%.

Rules for rounding off digits other than five, or of several digits, follow from the demand of a minimum error caused by rounding off: rounding off a five followed only by zeros leads to the same error if it is done upwards or downwards, and therefore the very old custom is adhered to, i.e. rounding off to an even number, although there is no mathematical reason for so doing.

Finally, errors caused by rounding off should be mentioned. Consideration must be given to when numerical values should be rounded off and when not. It holds in general that rounding off is permissible only if the relative error caused by rounding off is small compared with the error of the analysis. For example, errors caused by rounding off equivalents, calculation factors and final results are slight to such an extent that they need not be considered at all in practical work. HILLEBRAND et al. [16] state – and certainly their view is correct – that it is useless to employ calculation factors which have been calculated with a precision far exceeding the precision which can be guaranteed for the result of the analysis, i.e. roughly 0.05 % relative. For example, the precision of the gravimetric determination of iron as iron(III) oxide would not be harmed at all, if a rounded-off value of 0.7 were used instead of the value 0.6994 which is given in tables. The same holds for the value of 0.42 instead of 0.4202 for sulphuric acid determined as barium sulphate, etc. On the other hand, it is wrong to round off values obtained by measurement; instead, their complete value must be used in the calculation and only the final result may be rounded off. Perhaps only if a large sample is taken for a trace analysis are we justified in rounding off the sample weight before the calculation, as rounding it off to the number of decimal digits which will influence the final result can be done without loss of reliability.

Of the various *aids for numerical calculation* of results, a slide-rule suffices in normal work; a slide-rule 250 mm long will allow calculations with a precision of roughly 0.2 %. Only for the results of highly precise analyses, or the determination of constants (titre of a volumetric solution etc) is it better to use logarithmic tables. The precision of results calculated with the use of logarithmic tables is about 0.1 % for 4-figure tables, 0.01 % for 5-figure tables, and so on; 5-figure tables are quite adequate. A simple calculating machine is also very useful. Obviously gross errors (mistakes) may also occur in calculation: these may easily be avoided by checking the calculation. The fewer calculations there are to be done, the less is the possibility of a grave error of calculation occurring: therefore, utmost use should be made of tabulated data. To allow calculations to be checked even after some time, laboratory records should be written carefully, legibly and in a clear manner, and their arrangement should always be the same. All calculations should be written down in the laboratory record, and their scheme should be set down even if a slide-rule or a calculating machine is used. In some more complicated cases, e.g. when treating extensive experimental material by the least squares method or calculating the result of a multi-component analysis, it may be of advantage to use a digital computer [40, 53].

LITERATURE

BOOKS

1. AHRENS, L. H. and TAYLOR, S. R. *Spectrochemical Analysis*, 2nd Ed., Addison, London, 1961.
2. BELL, D. A. *Information Theory and Its Engineering Application*, 2nd Ed., Pitman, London, 1956.
3. BRILLOUIN, L. *Scientific Uncertainty and Information*, Academic Press, New York, 1964.
4. CRAMER, H. *Mathematical Methods of Statistics*, Princeton University Press, 1964.
5. CRUMPLER, T. B. and YOE, H. J. *Chemical Computation and Errors*, Wiley, New York, 1946.
6. DAVIES, O. L. *Statistical Methods in Research and Production*, 2nd Ed., Oliver and Boyd, London, 1954.
7. DOERFFEL, KL. *Beurteilung von Analysenverfahren und Ergebnissen*, Springer, Berlin, 1962.
8. DOERFFEL, KL. *Statistik in der analytischen Chemie*, VEB Deutscher Verlag für Grundstoffindustrie, Leipzig, 1966.
9. DUVAL, C. *Inorganic Thermogravimetric Analysis*, 2nd Ed., Elsevier, Amsterdam, 1963.
10. ECKSCHLAGER, K. *Grafické metody v analytické chemii*, SNTL, Prague; 1966.
11. GORDON, L., SALUTSKY, M. L. and WILLARD, H. H. *Precipitation from Homogeneous Solution*, Wiley, New York, 1959.
12. GOTTSCHALK, G. *Statistik in der quantitativen chemischen Analyse*, Enke, Stuttgart, 1962.
13. GOTTSCHALK, G. *Einführung in die Grundlagen der chemischen Materialprüfung*, Hirtzel, Stuttgart, 1966.
14. HALD, A. *Statistical Theory with Engineering Applications*, Wiley, New York, 1952.
15. HÄGG, G. *Die theoretischen Grundlagen der analytischen Chemie*, 4th Ed., Birkhäuser, Basel, 1966.
16. HILLEBRAND, W. F., LUNDELL, G. E. F., BRIGHT, H. A. and HOFFMANN, J. I. *Applied Inorganic Analysis*, Wiley, New York, 1953.
17. HEYROVSKÝ, J. and KŮTA, J.: *Principles of Polarography*, Academic Press, London, 1965.
18. HOVORKA, V. *Obecné úvahy a manipulace (General Considerations and Basic Operations)*, Czechoslovak Chemical Society, Prague, 1948.
19. KOLTHOFF, I. M. and LINGANE, J. *Polarography*, Interscience, New York, 1941.
20. KOLTHOFF, I. M. and ELVING, P. J. *Treatise on Analytical Chemistry*, Interscience, New York, 1959—1967.
21. KORTÜM, G. *Kolorimetrie, Photometrie und Spektrometrie*, 4th Ed., Springer, Berlin, 1962.
22. LAITINEN, H. A. *Chemical Analysis*, McGraw-Hill, New York, 1960.
23. LINDER, A. *Statistische Methoden für Naturwissenschaftler, Mediziner und Ingenieure*, 3th Ed., Birkhäuser, Basel, 1960.
24. MANDEL, J. *The Statistical Analysis of Experimental Data*, Interscience, New York, 1964.
25. NALIMOV, V. V. *The Application of Mathematical Statistics to Chemical Analysis*, Pergamon, London, 1963.
26. RINGBOM, A. *Complexation in Analytical Chemistry*, Interscience, New York, 1963.

27. SEEL, F. *Grundlagen der analytischen Chemie*, 4th Ed., Verlag Chemie, Weinheim, 1965.
28. SANDELL, E. B. *Colorimetric Determination of Traces of Metals*, 3th Ed., Interscience, New York, 1959.
29. SIEGEL, S. *Nonparametric Statistics*, McGraw-Hill, New York, 1956.
30. SMITH, T. B. *Analytical Processes*, Arnold, London, 1946.
31. SCHWARZENBACH, G. *Die komplexometrischen Titrationen*, 2nd Ed., Enke, Stuttgart, 1956.
32. TOMÍČEK, O. *Chemické indikátory (Chemical Indicators)*, JČMF, Prague, 1946.
33. TREADWELL, W. D. *Tabellen zur quantitativen Analyse*, Deuticke, Vienna, 1938.
34. WALD, A. *Sequential Analysis*, Wiley, New York, 1947.
34a. WILCOXON, F. *Some Rapid Approximate Statistical Procedures*, Ann. Reviews Inc., Stanford, 1949.
35. YOUDEN, W. J. *Statistical Methods for Chemists*, 2nd Ed., Wiley, New York, 1951.
36. *Balances, Weights and Precise Laboratory Weighing*, D.S.I.R. Notes on Applied Science No 7; HMSO; 1962.

JOURNALS:

37. AGTERDENBOS, J. *Anal. Chim. Acta* **15**, 429 (1956)
37a. ANFÄLT, J. and JAGNER, D. *Talanta* **16**, 555 (1969)
38. AYRES G. H. *Anal. Chem.* **21**, 652 (1949).
39. BARANSKA, H. *Chem. Anal. (Warsaw)* **6**, 1061 (1961).
40. BARNETT, H. A. and BARTOLI, A. *Anal. Chem.* **32**, 1153 (1960).
41. BLADE, E. *Ind. Eng. Chem., Anal. Ed.* **12**, 330 (1940).
42. BENEŠ, M. and ECKSCHLAGER, K. *Chem. listy* **54**, 1089 (1060).
43. CLANCEY, V. J. *Nature* **159**, 339 (1947).
44. CHALMERS, R. A. and CURNOW, R. N. *Analyst* **89**, 567 (1964).
45. CHLOPIN, V. G. *Z. anorg. allgem. Chem.* **143**, 1, 17 (1925).
46. DEAN, R. B. and DIXON, W. J. *Anal. Chem.* **23**, 636 (1951).
47. DOERFFEL, KL. *Z. anal. Chem.* **157**, 195, 241 (1957).
48. DOERFFEL, KL. *Chem. Technik* **10**, 151 (1958).
49. DOERNER, H. A. and HOSKINS, W. M. *J. Am. Chem. Soc.* **47**, 662 (1925).
50. ECKSCHLAGER, K. *Collection Czech. Chem. Commun.* **25**, 987 (1960).
51. ECKSCHLAGER, K. *Collection Czech. Chem. Commun.* **27**, 1521 (1962).
52. ECKSCHLAGER, K. *Chem. listy* **54**, 1133 (1960).
53. ECKSCHLAGER, K. *Chem. listy* **57**, 812 (1963).
54. ECKSCHLAGER, K. *Chem. listy* **61**, 592 (1967).
55. ECKSCHLAGER, K. *Chem. průmysl* **10**, 585 (1960).
56. ECKSCHLAGER, K. *Chem. průmysl* **12**, 136 (1961).
57. ECKSCHLAGER, K. *Chem. průmysl* **12**, 244 (1962).
58. ECKSCHLAGER, K. *Čs. farmacie* **13**, 468 (1964).
59. EHRLICH, G. and GERBATSCH, R. *Reinstoffe in Wissenschaft und Technik, International Symposium*, Dresden 1961, p. 421.
60. EHRLICH, G. and GERBATSCH, R. *Z. anal. Chem.* **209**, 35 (1965).
61. FAUSS, R. *Z. anal. Chem.* **155**, 11 (1957).
62. FLASCHKA, H. and KHALAFALLAH, S. *Z. anal. Chem.* **156**, 401 (1957).
63. GOTTSCHALK, G. and DEHMEL, P. *Z. anal. Chem.* **159**, 81 (1957).
64. GOTTSCHALK, G. and DEHMEL, P. *Z. anal. Chem.* **160**, 161 (1958).
65. GOTTSCHALK, G. and DEHMEL, P. *Z. anal. Chem.* **163**, 273, 330 (1958).
66. HIGUCHI, T., REHM, C. and BARNSTEIN, C. *Anal. Chem.* **28**, 1506 (1956).
67. HOLDT, G. and STRASHEIM, A. *Spectroscopy* **14**, 64 (1960).
68. ILKOVIČ, D. *Collection Czech. Chem. Commun.* **6**, 498 (1934).
69. KAISER, H. *Z. anal. Chem.* **209**, 1 (1965).
70. KAISER, H. *Z. anal. Chem.* **216**, 80 (1966).
71. KAISER, H. and SPECKER, H. *Z. anal. Chem.* **149**, 46 (1956).
72. KIENITZ, H. *Z. anal. Chem.* **164**, 80 (1958).
73. KÖRBL, J. and PŘIBIL, R. *Chem. listy* **52**, 601 (1958).
74. LIEBHAFSKY, H. A., PFEIFFER, H. A. and BALLIS, E. W. *Anal. Chem.* **23**, 5131 (1951).
75. LORD, E. *Biometrika* **34**, 41 (1947).
76. LÜPKE, A. VON *Chemiker-Ztg.* **80**, 875 (1956).
77. MANDEL, J. and LINNING, F. J. *Anal. Chem.* **28**, 770 (1956).
78. MAURICE, M. J. *Z. anal. Chem.* **158**, 271 (1957).

79. MEITES, L. *Anal. Chem.* **28**, 139 (1957).
80. PLŠKO, E. *Acta Chim. Acad. Sci. Hung.* **32**, 419 (1962).
81. PLŠKO, E. *Revue Roumaine de Chimie* **10**, 605 (1965).
82. REILLEY, C. N. and SCHMID, R. W. *Anal. Chem.* **31**, 887 (1959).
83. REINMUTH, W. H. *Anal. Chem.* **28**, 1956 (1956).
84. RINGBOM, A. and WÄNNINEN, E. *Anal. Chim. Acta* **11**, 153 (1954).
85. ROOS, J. B. *Analyst* **87**, 832 (1962).
86. RUBEŠKA, I. *Chem. listy* **59**, 1119 (1965).
87. SHEWELL, C. T. *Anal. Chem.* **31**, No. 5, 21 A (1959).
88. SCHEJTANOV, CHR. *Anal. Chim. Acta* **17**, 263 (1957).
89. SCHRÖER, E. *Naturwissenschaften* **25**, 81 (1937).
90. SCHMID, R. W. and REILLEY C. N. *Anal. Chem.* **29**, 264 (1957).
91. SPRENT, P. *Nature* **187**, 438 (1960).
92. "STUDENT" (W. G. GOSSET) *Biometrika* **6**, 1 (1908).
93. STURM, F. VON; *Z. anal. Chem.* **166**, 100 (1959).
94. SVEHLA, G., PÁLL, A. and ERDEY L. *Talanta* **10**, 719 (1963).
95. SVOBODA, V., GERBATSCH, R. *Z. anal. Chem.* **242**, 1 (1968).
95a. WÄNNINEN, E. *Talanta* **15**, 717 (1968).
96. WEIMARN, P. P. VON *Chem. Reviews* **2**, 217 (1926).
97. WELCH, B. L. *J. Am. Statist. Assoc* **53**, 777 (1958).
98. WILSON, A. L. *Analyst* **86**, 72 (1961).
99. WINEFORDNER, J. D. and VICKERS T. J. *Anal. Chem.* **36**, 1939 (1964). JOHN, P. A. S,
    McCARTHY, W. J. and WINEFORDNER, J. D. *Anal. Chem.* **39**, 1945 (1967).
100. WOKROJ, A. *Chem. Anal. (Warsaw)* **11**, 838 (1966).
101. YOUDEN, W. J. *Anal. Chem.* **19**, 946 (1947).
102. YOUDEN, W. J. *Analyst* **77**, 974 (1952).

INDEX